A HARBOUR GOES TO WAR

The story of Mulberry and the men who made it happen

Published by Brook House Publishing
for the South Machars Historical Society
Garlieston, Wigtownshire

Produced in Scotland by
Brook House Publishing
Garlieston
Wigtownshire

for The South Machars Historical Society

A Harbour Goes to War
ISBN 1 873547 30 7

Designed and Typeset by Brook House Publishing Services, Garlieston, Wigtownshire
Text Octavian MT
Printed by Bath Press, Glasgow

CONTENTS

ACKNOWLEDGEMENTS

Special thanks are due to Mrs Jane Evans of The South Machars Historical Society (SMHS), Garlieston, for unswervingly pursuing the cause, and for collecting myriad letters, photographs, publications and articles relating to the Mulberry Harbours. Without her charm and determination, this publication would never have come about. Thanks also to T C McCreath and K J Palmer for their valuable time and support.

We would like to thank everyone who contributed, in whatever form, to the making of this book. Reading all the accounts has given all involved considerable pleasure. In order to create a thread of continuity, avoid inevitable repetition of facts, and stick to budget we have, regrettably, had to exclude many interesting accounts and illustrations. It is, however, the intention of SMHS to make all the material available in a forthcoming CD publication. And if the objectives of this project are achieved, a permanent exhibition site will be found in Wigtownshire.

In addition we would like to thank the following for allowing us to reproduce their accounts or copyrighted material:

Lady Butter, CVO, daughter of Maj. Gen. Sir Harold Wernher KVO
The family of the late Sir Bruce White
Sir Alan Harris CBE
Allan H Beckett, MBE., FICE., BSc.
George Youngs, Chief Designer of Lobnitz & Co., Ltd.
Fred Lobnitz, son of Mr Pearson Lobnitz
Mrs. Lyn Black, daughter of Lt. Col. R J P Cowan
Dr. William Lind of the Ballast Trust
Guy Hartcup, author
Thomas R Coughtrie, Electrical Engineer to Mulberry components
A T Murchie
John Guy
Major General C A Ramsay, son of Admiral Sir Bertram Ramsay
David Ramsay, son of Admiral Sir Bertram Ramsay
John H Proud, author of *Seahorses of the Tees*
Robin Stirling, ex Editor of *The Motherwell Times*
Major Edwin Hunt, Emeritus Bargemaster
Institution of Engineers & Shipbuilders in Scotland
Imperial War Museum
Motherwell Bridge Holdings
Dr. John Rhodes of The Royal Engineers Museum
Institution of Civil Engineers

North Lanarkshire Council, Leisure Services
Ministry of Defence
Churchill Archives Centre
Royal Archives, Windsor
Bodleian Library
Royal National Lifeboat Institution, Clovelly branch
Waverley Excursions Ltd. Glasgow
Royal Commission on the Ancient & Historical Monuments of Scotland
The Military Engineer, USA
Cory Ship Towage Ltd.
Brigadier A E M Walter, CBE
Captain Jack Niblock
Raymond Dierkes – Seabee USA Construction Battalion
Robert Pintar – Seabee USA Construction Battalion
Mrs. Ann Bartlett
David McIntyre – son of Lt. H C McIntyre
Owens Elliot – Royal Marines
W J Boyle, brother of the late Harold Boyle
Richard Polglaze and Alan Brown – authors of *HMS Aristocrat*
Walter King Webster – Kites & Balloon Forces
Mrs. Barbara Scott-Jupp – Nurse with QAIMNS
J McKenzie
B Stewart

Major Allan H Beckett

FOREWORD

Perhaps the earliest beginnings of Mulberry Harbour go back to the Gallipoli campaign of 1915.

There the allies experienced the greatest difficulties supplying an army from the sea, and partly for this reason suffered a serious defeat. The campaign was largely the brainchild of Winston Churchill, and he was severely criticised subsequently. No doubt he often thought over the lessons of this episode during the years between the wars when it seemed as though his active career was over. Whether or not the idea of a portable harbour was originally his, his unhesitating support and conviction ensured that it was built.

Like the Trojan horse, Mulberry is an example of one of those completely original ideas in warfare that can only ever be used once in history. The enemy had not considered it even remotely possible that an invasion could be supported by an artificial harbour, assembled and working within a few days. Without the element of surprise it could not have been done. Once done, it can never be done again.

My life in the Royal Engineers was changed utterly from the moment my Commanding Officer, Colonel W T Everall, OBE showed me Churchill's famous directive:

> **Piers for flat beaches**
> They must float up and down with the tide.
> The anchor problem must be mastered.
> Let me have the best solution worked out.
> Don't argue the matter, the difficulties will
> argue for themselves.'

Col. Everall said: 'Sailing is your hobby, Beckett — perhaps you can think of something that will solve this problem'

Within a week my design for the 'Whale' roadway was made, first as a tin model, then later full scale. The full size, 6 span prototype was built and tested in a storm at Garlieston in Scotland.

I obtained permission to go over to Arromanches on the first tow, as it was important for me to see that the 'Whale' was correctly assembled from its component parts.

The satisfaction of seeing my roadways made up and in constant use cannot be overestimated. I am sure that the success of my design owes much to Col. Everall, his encouragement, and his generosity in giving me this unique opportunity.

When Mulberry was no longer needed the floating roadways were dismantled and reused in the many bridging repairs needed in newly liberated Europe. The block ships were also salvaged for scrap so at Arromanches today only the slowly decaying remains of the Phoenixes are to be seen out at sea, together with the wreckage of an intermediate pontoon and a few concrete float units on the beach. However the visitor to this peaceful little French town cannot fail to be impressed by the scale of these scattered remnants. They are reminders of a tremendous undertaking which, through the efforts of many thousands of people, overcame immense administrative and engineering difficulties to play a key role in the defeat of tyranny.

Allan Beckett
May 2000

PREFACE

There is a saying that 'old men forget'. They and their deeds shall never be forgotten. — Anon

Some people may look on this publication as a grand chapter of military history or engineering achievement, or a prime example of the strategic implications of total war: it is all these and more. It is an insight into the minds of the men, groups and individuals at all levels who met unprecedented challenges and prevailed.

It should be acknowledged that great credit should go to those in authority who picked and appointed these very special men, civilian and military, to command, inspire and lead, whose affirmative actions were crucial when the pressure was greatest.

A Harbour Goes to War traces the Mulberry project from conception to completion; through design, testing and manufacturing, to the immense logistical problems of moving men and materials to the beaches of Normandy. And, when they were there, securing in the face of near disaster, a crucial beachhead that decided the outcome of the War in Europe. Those who were involved delivered innovative solutions to complex problems against near impossible deadlines, and in the process often exerted themselves to the limits of human endurance.

Looking back we can, and should, marvel at the brilliance of the original concept underlying the project, and the spontaneous enthusiasm of those who were asked to help. This was the biggest collaborative construction undertaking ever attempted in war or peace. It involved sites and companies all over Britain. The accounts of the assembly on the south coast, the delivery and planting in Normandy, and the superhuman efforts in the face of the storm are sagas in their own right.

Through the eyes of some who were there, this is the story of Mulberry, and the men who made it happen.

Top left: Mr. Thomas R Coughtrie
Top right: Lt. Col R J P Cowan
Bottom left: Admiral Sir Bertram Ramsay
Bottom right: Brig. A E M Walter

PERSONAE

Alexander, Rt. Hon. A V, CH, MP	First Lord of the Admiralty
Badger, Admiral USN	In charge of supplies
Beckett, Major Allan H	Assistant to Lt. Col. Everall, main designer of floating bridges. Sent as technical assistant in the Field to 21 Army Group
Bernal, Prof. J D	Professor of Physics and Crystallography: one of Mountbatten's scientific advisers
Bevin, Rt. Hon. Ernest	Minister for Labour
Bunting, Col. T B	Assistant to Sir Harold Wernher
Carline, Major J G (later Lt. Col.)	In charge of Cairn Head camp for training in assembly of pierheads
Court, Major R J, CE	Second in command to Lt. Col. Mais
Cowan, Lt. Col. R J P (Ronnie)	Commander of 969 & 970 Companies who planted floating piers and roadways
Clark, Capt. A Dayton, USN	Commander Force 128 in charge of the Seabees
Cunningham, Admiral Sir Andrew, RN	First Sea Lord
Duncan, Sir Andrew	Minister for Supply
Eisenhower, General Dwight D	Supreme Allied Commander of SHAEF (Supreme Headquarters Allied Expeditionary Force
Ellsberg, Commander Edward USN	In charge of salvage clearance
Everall, R E, Lt. Col.	Chief Bridging Instructor
Faber, Dr. Oscar	Expert in concrete
Gale, Lt. Gen. Sir Humfrey	Chief Administrator under General Eisenhower
Gilbert, Col. S K	Deputy Commander of the British Mulberry Task Force
Gibson, John (Later Sir John)	In charge of production of the Phoenixes

Hamilton, Ronald M — Inventor of the Swiss Roll

Harris, Major Alan — In command of advance party of 933 Port Construction & Repair Coy. RE

Heming, John (US) — In command of US Motor Towing Launch (MTL), worked with J Luck

Hickling, Vice Admiral Harold, CBE DSO — Naval Liaison Officer to Maj. Gen. Wernher, later appointed Naval Officer in Charge Mulberry Harbour

Hill, Capt. L B, RN — In command of blockships leaving Oban

Hinrichs, Maj. Andrew H — In command of 935 Port Construction & Repair Coy. & Demolition

Hobart, Sir Percy — Eminent tank expert

Hughes, Iorys — Welsh consulting engineer: inventor of the Hippo

Hughes-Hallett, Vice Admiral, John — Chief Naval Planner Combined Operations: apparently the first to envisage a harbour on the model of Mulberry

Hunt, Major Edwin — Operated barges

Hussey, Capt. T, RN — COHQ, experimented with the Bubble breakwater

Jarman, Lt. W D (Jim) — Commanded a Landing Barge Engineering of 36th Supply Repair Flotilla

Jellet, Capt. J H, RNVR — Deputy in command of the British Mulberry Task Force

King, Maj. Gen. Charles J S — Engineer in Chief

Lampen, Lt. Cdr. A M D, RN — In charge of planting the third Gooseberry

Leathers, Lord Frederick Alan — Chairman of Wm. Cory & Son Ltd., (Tug towage) and other Cory subsidiary companies

Leigh Mallory, Air Marshal Sir Trafford — Commander Allied Expeditionary Force

Lobnitz, Pearson — Owner and Chairman of Lobnitz & Co., Shipbuilders & Dredger Designers, Renfrew

Lochner, Lt. Cdr. R A — DMWD: took part in lilo trial, subsequently responsible for Bombardons

Luck, Capt. John	In command of British tugs and tows
McMullen, General Donald J, RE	Director of Transportation War Office
Macready, Gen. Sir Gordon	On Combined Staff in Washington
Mais, Lt. Col. Raymond	Bristish Expeditionary Force. Personal Deputy to Brigadier Walter: in charge of construction of piers and pierheads
Metcalfe, Sir Ralph Ismay	Director of Sea Transport
Morgan, Gen. Sir Frederick	Supreme Commander (Designate): Deputy Chief of Staff to Supreme Commander Allied Expeditionary Force
Petrie, Capt. C H, RN	Hydrographer: in charge of Naval side of planting Mulberry B
Ramsay, Admiral Sir Bertram	Allied Naval Commander in Chief, Expeditionary Force
Riddell-Webster, Gen. Thomas S	Quarter Master General to the Forces, War Office
Robson, Mr P W	Chairman of Alexander Findlay & Co., Motherwell, Construction Engineers of 14 Spud Pontoons
Sainsbury, Lt. Col J R	Worked with Col. Mais: responsible for inspection and progress of Whale pier
Scott-Bowden, Maj. Gen. L	Combined Operations (COPP): beach reconnaissance and assault pilotage parties
Steer-Webster, Lt. Col. Vassal C, RE	On General Riddell-Webster's staff. Devised concrete mattress called 'hards', also at Garlieston and Cairn Head
Tarling, Capt. George, RE	Captain in 969 & 970 companies to plant floating piers
Tedder, Air Chief Marshal, Sir Arthur	Deputy Supreme Commander
Tennant, Rear Admiral (later Vice Admiral) William G	In charge of movement and erection of Mulberry

Tonks, Major D J, RE	In charge of 167 Railway Bridging Coy. and 970 Equipment Coy, at Cairn Head
Vaughan, Brig. Gen. H B	US Engineers: appointed as liaison officer with the Admiralty
Vian, Rear Admiral, Sir Philip, VC	Commander of the British Invasion Fleet
Wake-Walker, Vice Admiral Sir Frederic	Controller, Admiralty
Walter, Brig. A E Mervyn, CBE	Director of Ports and Inland Waterways, 21 Army Group
Wernher, Maj. Gen. Sir Harold	COSSAC: appointed co-ordinator (1943) of Ministry & Science facilities, in overall charge of construction of Mulberry Harbour
White, Brigadier, (later Sir) Bruce, KBE	Assistant Director of Transportation: suggested to Churchill the concept of the dredger as basis for a floating harbour
Winn, Rt. Hon. Reggie	ADC to Field Marshal Sir John Dill
Youngs, George	Chief Designer of the Spud Pontoon at Lobnitz, Renfrew

GLOSSARY

Beetle	Steel, and later concrete, pontoons used for supporting bridging sections. A component of the floating roadway.
Bombardons	Cruciform floating barrages used for wave supression. One of three elements of the Mulberry breakwater.
Breakwater	Provided sheltered water within the Mulberry harbour. Comprised three elements: Phoenix caissons, Bombardons and blockships.
COHQ	Combined Operations Headquarters.
COPP	Combined Operations Beach Reconnaissance and Assault Pilotage Parties.
Corncob	Codename applied to assembly, fitting out and sailing of blockships.
COSSAC	Chief of Staff to Supreme Allied Commander.
Crocodiles	Tubular steel span for Hughes pier.
D-day	Day of invasion; D-day+1, one day after initial assault; D-day+2, etc.
DMWD	Department of Miscellaneous Weapon Development, Admiralty.
DUKW	American amphibious vehicles: D — year (1942); U — Utility; K — front-wheel drive; W — two rear driving axles. Known as 'ducks'.
Erection tank	Steel float used for positioning and connection of floating roadway sections.
Gooseberry	Line of sunken ships, positioned to provide sheltered water.
Hippo	Concrete caisson that formed part of Hughes pier, one of the three Mulberry prototypes.
IWT	Inland Water Transport.
Kite anchor	Special anchor designed by Allan Beckett. Used for anchoring the floating roadway component of the Whale piers. A development of the CQR (codename for secure) anchor used by the LSTs.

KBO	Kite and Balloons officer.
LCT	Landing Craft (Tank).
LST	Landing Ship (Tank).
MTL	Motor Towing Launch.
Mulberry	Codename given to the artificial ports designed for the D-day invasion.
Mulberry A	The American Mulberry port.
Mulberry B	The British Mulberry port.
Overlord	Codename for the plan to invade Europe.
PCF	Port Construction Force.
Phoenix	Large concrete caisson made in different sizes. Sunk on site to form part of breakwater.
QAIMNS	Queen Alexandra's Imperial Military Nursing Service.
RE	Royal Engineers.
RN	Royal Navy.
Roundup	Original codename for what became Overlord.
Seabees	The US Navy's construction battalion. No equivalent in Royal Navy.
Slug	Surf Landing Under Girder.
Spud Pontoon	Floating pierhead with legs that could be raised and lowered individually, depending on the state of the tide.
Swiss Roll	Floating roadways with 'hinged' sides to prevent the ingress of water.
Tn5	Transportation 5 of the Directorate of Transportation, War Office.
Whale	Codename given to floating pierheads and roadways used in Mulberry.

OPENING SCENES

When it came to invading the Continent we had two enemies to reckon
with: one was the Germans, the other was the weather. Of these two
enemies by far the most unpredictable, the most uncertain — more
capricious than any woman — was the weather. As the 'Sailing
Directions' — the sailors' Bible — says: 'The weather in the English
Channel is seldom calm.'
   — Vice Admiral H Hickling CBE, DSO

This judgement upon the dual enemies facing the combined forces of Great Britain
and America was made when it became clear that the re-invasion of Europe was, in
the opinion of the commanders concerned, the best possible strategy to bring the
war to a successful conclusion. Various plans for the second front were proposed by
the commanders of both British and American forces, but finally, it was decided by
the Spring of 1943, that a major operation against the Continent — subsequently
called Overlord — should be mounted by means of an invasion of the Northern
French coast. The choice of a suitable area proved difficult. Vice Admiral Hickling
explains the problem.

> The landing of a huge army with a 'build-up' of millions of tons of
> equipment and stores called for all the appliances of a major port. We
> might, of course, land over open beaches but that would put the ' build-
> up' at the mercy of the weather. General Sir Frederick Morgan, COSSAC,
> as he was called in those far-off days of August 1943, was Chief of Staff
> to the Supreme Allied Commander who was then undesignated — later
> to be General Eisenhower. Either of these courses of action was acceptable
> to him. Hitler had said, 'If we hold the ports we hold Europe', and the
> Germans meant to hold the ports: we had had a taste of assaulting a
> major port at Dieppe. To have attacked Cherbourg, for instance, would
> have been a costly, lengthy and bloody business, forfeiting any element of
> surprise. Nor was the alternative of landing over open beaches acceptable
> because no prudent commander was going to leave his 'build-up' to the
> mercy of the weather in the English Channel.

Most commanders and senior officers were in complete agreement with the
acuteness of the difficulties, however aware they had become of the necessity of
mounting an invasion. Sir Alan Harris not only explains the situation in somewhat
pessimistic terms, but also adds a gloss from his knowledge of attempted invasions
of the past to add weight to the expression of his fears.

> Ideas, politics, planning and the practicalities governing the fortunes of
> war were in a state of flux not easily distinguishable from chaos and not
> helped by inter-service rivalry. It was apparent that naval blockade

would not win the war; air bombardment might in the long run but the enemy had new and powerful weapons nearly ready. Delay was perilous. So it had to be invasion.

History offered no encouragement: Xerxes failed despite his bridge of boats across the Dardanelles; the Spanish Armada never even landed and the following year, Drake, with as big a fleet and a bigger army failed dismally to restore the king of Portugal to his throne. William succeeded at Hastings with the help of all-but-incredible good fortune. Seaborne raids are commonplace; seaborne invasions are known but it is rare that nations have been conquered thereby. In the words of General Bradley, 'You can always force an invasion but you can't always make it stick.'

The capture of a major port had been rejected on several counts, before the raid on Dieppe of August 18th. Even with sea and air command, the powerful defences, which could be expected in north-west Europe, would be difficult to overcome (a consideration confirmed by Dieppe). The enemy would be able to hold out long enough to render the port unusable for months, as happened with Cherbourg, while the attack itself could destroy the facilities of the port, as happened at Le Havre and at Brest. There had to be some other way.

By the early 1940s the Allies had specialised equipment for assault on beaches and were experienced in its use, but once the inevitable counter-attack was resisted we still had to land and supply an army large enough to confront and vanquish the powerful forces that were awaiting it. For an assault, the right moment could be chosen, but how useful would the beaches be in the long term? They would be useless in onshore winds, and since craft would have to be beached and await the next tide for refloating, their potential would be limited. Furthermore, how would the beaches stand up to repeated use? As it was, the Landing Ships (tanks) soon began to suffer from the debris of war that already littered the sands.

The choice between attempting to capture a major port, or attempting to land men, machines, equipment and supplies, over a period of time, on an open beach, was made, but in favour of beach landings. The problem, once that decision had been made, was how to carry them out. In essence, in the summer of 1942, the Allies had decided upon the 'What', the 'Where', and the 'When', but had no firm idea of the all-important 'How'. How could such complex landings be achieved?

The first, and no doubt very startling suggestion for solving the question of How, appears to have come from Captain, later Vice Admiral John Hughes-Hallett, RN, who was then Chief Naval Planner at Combined Operations. It had an elegant and most misleading simplicity. 'If,' he said 'there were no harbours in the area selected, they should be manufactured'. It is true that a good deal of work had already been done on the planning and construction of artificial harbours; as Major-General Sir Harold Wernher, Chief of Staff Supreme Allied Commander had stated, Captain T

Hussey, RN, COHQ had experimented with a Bubble breakwater. The War Office had a panel of civil engineers who had been working on a plan to solve this problem [of construction]. Furthermore, a prototype pierhead of steel had been constructed which could be used in conjunction with a floating roadway to unload ships up to a draught of eighteen feet. The 'panel of civil engineers' to which Sir Harold makes reference, was led by Sir Bruce White, KBE, who explains when, and for what purpose it was created.

> Early 1941 a new branch of the War Office was formed under my direction and given the title Transportation 5, or Tn5 as it was known. Tn5 was given the job of controlling the port construction and repair and maintenance companies as well as administering the port repair ships, dredgers, floating cranes; port operation and the construction of certain railways. Tn5's initial responsibility was the creation of Military Ports Numbers 1 and 2.
>
> The experience gained there and the resulting organisation, particularly the training of military personnel, was to be used to the full in the planning, design, construction, assembly and testing of all the engineered elements for the invasion of 'Fortress Europe'.

The truly amazing consequence in which all this planning was to culminate, was that the artificial harbours which had been constructed in a variety of sites all over Britain, should be assembled and towed across the Channel to be erected on the beaches of Arromanches and Omaha. It was a plan of breath-taking audacity, which, when it was first proposed was by no means well received. Different commanders, in different services, each had their own favourite plan for both the invasion site and the means to invade. Agreement seemed impossible until, finally, at the Largs Conference, which was held on 23rd August, 1943, Lord Mountbatten managed to achieve consensus; and the use of artificial, and, indeed, transportable harbours was approved. Major-General Sir Harold Wernher explains how this came about.

> During the summer of 1942, very active planning was in progress. In the first place operation Sledgehammer, which was an attack to be launched by six divisions on the French coast, was being considered. Admiral Sir Bertie Ramsay was brought up from Dover in order to carry out the Naval planning. This was subsequently abandoned when the North African operation was mounted. Meanwhile an administration planning committee was set up under Lt.General Sir Humfrey Gale in order to plan Roundup, which was the major operation against the Continent and was subsequently called Overlord. Although much useful research work was done, there were over fifty Committees, with more than thirty members on each, so it was almost impossible to get any agreement or decision. However, the preliminary work was useful to General Morgan when he became Chief of Staff to the Supreme Allied Commander.

As the summer progressed, the planning for Roundup proceeded energetically. I was called in to several of the operational meetings attended by General Paget, Air Chief Marshal Sir Sholto Douglas and Admiral Mountbatten. It was clear from the commencement that Paget and Sholto Douglas did not think an invasion of the Continent could take place against any portions of the French coast except the Calais-Boulogne area, chiefly owing to the difficulty of providing air cover due to the limited range of fighter aircraft. Mountbatten was bitterly opposed to this plan and stated that the only part of the French coast which was lightly defended was in the neighbourhood of Cherbourg. He stated that it should be possible to increase the range of fighter aircraft by some means such as subsidiary petrol tanks. General Paget pointed out that there were no harbours capable of supporting an offensive in that area and that those which existed would certainly be destroyed. Mountbatten replied that even that problem could be solved and that he would put up a further plan. It was in fact made possible by the construction of the Mulberry harbours.

In the spring of 1943, the COSSAC plan, which was to be presented in August at the Quebec conference, called Quadrant, was well advanced; it was based on Mountbatten's original conception for an attack in the Cherbourg area, but there was still opposition from the original planners of Roundup. Mountbatten then conceived the brilliant idea of holding a Conference at Largs, to which he would invite all those who had been interested in any planning, such as the COSSAC staff, General Paget, the Admiralty and the RAF, the idea being to discuss landing operations in general and the COSSAC plan which General Morgan had prepared.

During the first two or three days of the Conference, it was clear that Mountbatten was on a very sticky wicket. However, by his forceful personality and charm, he was able to persuade all present that the COSSAC plan was the right one, provided the three main principles were observed, namely, complete air and sea protection and artificial harbours. With regard to the last named, the following minute was sent to the Chiefs of Staff:

> That a single authority should be appointed who, in consultation with the Service Departments, will tackle the whole problem of the construction of special piers (of which one design has already been produced) to accelerate unloading on the beaches. A decision is urgently needed as to the types and numbers required. This authority should also deal with the provision of artificial ports and breakwaters and the development of those Continental ports we shall capture.

The question of How, had been answered. The construction of Mulberry was about to start.

PLANNING

© Imperial War Museum, London

10, Downing Street
Whitehall.

PIERS FOR USE ON BEACHES

C.C.O.
or deputy.

They must float up and down with the tide. The anchor problem must be mastered. Let me have the best solution worked out. Don't argue the matter. The difficulties will argue for themselves.

30. 5. 42.

The Churchill memo that started it all.

It is clear, from this memo from the Prime Minster, that although the decision to land the invading forces from 'special Pierheads to accelerate unloading on the beaches', there was still very little clear understanding of how such piers should be constructed. Despite Sir Harold Wernher's assurances that the War Office had already been working on the construction of artificial harbours, with some success (see page 3) Sir Winston Churchill's directive suggests that some very fundamental problems had not, so far, been addressed. One of these problems was ensuring the stability of safety of piers which were designed to be used on beaches with a tidal rise and fall of some magnitude, and which were also open to rough seas. Sir Bruce White as War Office representative was shown the Prime Minister's memo at a Combined Operations meeting under Lord Louis Mountbatten, and immediately felt that he could provide 'the best solution'. He explains:

5

At one such meeting, a naval captain produced Sir Winston Churchill's memorandum concerning 'PIERS FOR USE ON BEACHES'. As representing the War Office, whose responsibility among others was the building of ports, I said that it was my duty to undertake action on the Prime Minister's instructions and accordingly took the memorandum away from the meeting for consideration.

In my view, the memorandum indicated that the Prime Minister was not satisfied that enough attention had been devoted to the subject. I therefore approached Sir Winston Churchill's office, where I had a brief conversation suggesting that I had the solution to his memorandum, and asked that I should be granted the opportunity to explain to Sir Winston the manner in which his memorandum would be dealt [with]. My request resulted in an invitation to Chequers, where, I was told, I would be given the opportunity to explain my plans.

. . . After dinner Sir Winston took me away so that I could explain my proposals for dealing with his memorandum. At the time, he had just signed an undertaking to the Russians that the Second Front would be opened later in the year, if conditions were right.

I told the Prime Minister that I had frequently been involved in dredging, and particularly the equipment used for dredging, through my work for my firm. I then explained about the dredger which had been seen working in the harbour at Valparaiso during 1924. A storm had broken out and all the ships in the harbour had foundered, with the exception of the dredger. This craft, built at Renfrew in Scotland, was fitted with three 'spuds' or legs. The able master of the dredger made use of the vessel's ability to be lifted up and down on the legs by raising her above the waves, thereby avoiding the water's turbulence.

Such a technique not only met his request that 'they must float up and down with the tide' but also answered the 'anchor problem', since the spuds would be firmly placed upon the seabed.

After this explanation and a description of the extensive work which my department had already deployed so far in this direction, the Prime Minister was satisfied that much had already been accomplished towards resolving the engineering problems associated with the invasion. I think that his confidence was gained and this surely resulted in the help which Sir Winston gave me throughout the following years.

In the light of subsequent events, it can now be stated firmly that the eventual success of the Mulberry landings was largely attributable to Sir Bruce's observations of the single dredger to remain afloat in Valparaiso in 1924, and to the deductions he made from its survival. As other problems of construction arose, answers to them began to emerge, and Sir Bruce was entrusted with more information concerning the eventual employment of the artificial harbours. As he said, the plan was maturing.

Thus the department continued its efforts to find engineering solutions to the problems of landing vast numbers of troops and munitions from artificial harbours. I had been told in absolute secrecy in July 1943 that the Normandy beaches were to be the site of the landings. At the same time that Tn5 was working on the artificial harbours, breakwaters, floating roadways and other components, different teams elsewhere were also conducting research, including the Admiralty — to a certain extent — and the Americans.

His mention of the Americans is a reminder that they too were involved in the planning for Mulberry, and that the first major joint planning conference was to be held in Quebec in August 1943. Sir Harold Wernher takes up the story.

In the middle of August I received instructions to proceed by air with eighteen Service and Civilian experts to the Quebec Conference. We travelled to Prestwick and embarked in a Liberator Bomber, arriving in Montreal eighteen hours later. It was an uncomfortable trip, as we had to lie alternately across the bottom of the plane so that each individual had a pair of boots either side of his head. There were no arrangements for food other than the sandwiches which we took with us. Amongst the party was a Professor W G Penney of the Imperial College, a noted mathematician. Whilst we were flying at high altitude, we were told to use oxygen, but Professor Penney continued to carry out calculations, refusing to use oxygen, until he became green in the face. On landing, he told me that he was testing his ability to be accurate at various altitudes. On arrival in Montreal we found there was no connection with Quebec, but the local Control Officer put a special plane at our disposal and we landed at Quebec soon after lunch.

The same evening we held our first meeting with the American officers who had been called together to study the problem of artificial harbours. I introduced the delegation, and then the senior American officer spoke; he said that General Marshall had asked for a report, which had been prepared, and which was being presented immediately. I asked them what experience they had in these matters and on what basis the report had been compiled, but received a very unsatisfactory reply. Whereupon I stated that, if the American representatives had been able to draw up a report without consultation with the British, I saw no object in the delegation remaining, and I would suggest that night to the Prime Minister that, unless the report was withdrawn, we should proceed back to England. Immediate confusion ensued and, after a hurried conference, the Americans decided to withdraw the report and we proceeded to expound our case.

During the Conference, Admiral Mountbatten introduced me to all the Chiefs of Staffs and other important Officers who were likely to be of

7

service. He certainly put me over in a manner which I did not deserve, but it was distinctly useful for I was thus able to have direct access to all these important people once I reached Washington.

One of my first tasks was to approach Admiral Ernest King with regard to the supply of American tugs which would be required to tow the equipment to France. Admiral King was a most interesting study. He considered that he had been the prime mover in building up the American Navy and was determined, at all costs, to avenge Pearl Harbour. He was extremely jealous of any other Navy playing any part in the operations, as he wanted the war to be won by the US Navy alone which, in his opinion, he had built up. Although Admiral King promised fifteen tugs, they eventually turned out to be of very inferior quality.

Before the Conference closed at Quebec, it was decided that my delegation should proceed to Washington immediately to thrash out the details of the plan which was to be submitted to the Combined Chiefs of Staff.

Sir Bruce White was also present at the Quebec Conference, at which, with his agreement a final date was set for the completion of the harbours. He says:

> In August and September 1943 a crucial conference was held in Canada and the USA finally to settle and agree the invasion plan, codenamed 'Overlord'. Sir Winston Churchill and a very considerable staff proceeded to America aboard the *Queen Mary*.
>
> Within a few days an urgent message came from Sir Winston Churchill, then in Quebec, asking myself and a party of experts to join him there. Myself, along with Mr Reginald Gwyther, Major General Wernher and Colonel Steer-Webster, made preparations to fly to Quebec to discuss the provisions for the invasion, in particular the artificial harbours.
>
> We went to Quebec to discuss among ourselves the plans which we had made and then proceeded to Washington to meet our American allies. The whole of Operation Overlord was examined and the proposals for producing the artificial harbours were discussed fully. The American chiefs of staff approved our provisions. It was then decided that there should be two artificial harbours, the American became Mulberry A and the British, Mulberry B. The meeting was conducted by General Marshall, who asked whether our arrangements were such that the harbours would be available by May 1944, the date fixed for the invasion.
>
> In view of the organisation which had already been created, consisting not only of the panel of expert advisers but also the extensive supporting military organisation, I gave an affirmative reply, subject to the availability of certain materials and a supply of tugs to tow the completed

sections. I felt a great responsibility in giving this reply but I was aware of the strength of the organisation at home.

Vice Admiral Hickling is even more explicit. He had not attended the Conference, but was awaiting its decision in London. The signal was received on 4th September 1943 prefaced 'Bigot, Most Secret', and 'telling us to get busy with two artificial harbours, one in the American Sector at a place called Saint Laurent to be known as Mulberry A and one in the British Sector at Arromanches, ten miles to the eastward, to be known as Mulberry B. The harbours were to be prefabricated in the United Kingdom, towed across the Channel and put down in fourteen days. Each was to be the size of Dover, which you will recollect took seven years to build. These two harbours were to supply between them at least 12,000 tons of stores a day, irrespective of the weather. That was only one third of the total the armies required each day, which was of the order of 40,000 tons, but there had to be a guarantee that no matter what happened, whether it blew or snowed, a proportion of the stores would be landed.'

This plan, which Hickling outlines, is given in some detail, but was, indeed a clear indication of what the harbours were eventually expected to achieve. As Sir Harold Wernher had indicated, the Combined Chiefs of Staff still had many decisions to make, and it was for this meeting that he and his delegation went from Quebec to Washington. Sir Harold takes up the story:

> It became apparent on arrival that the Americans were quite prepared to leave the main problem of the harbours to us, but they were very helpful in arranging experiments in water tanks, whereby, by means of air injections, various wave effects could be produced, using models to represent the equipment to be used. The great difficulty arose from the fact that the Secretariat was quite incapable of putting the reports into the form which the Chiefs of Staffs expected. It was therefore a great relief when Professor Bernal, who attended our meetings, offered to draft the various regulations. Bernal was one of the few men who had ever been to Arromanches where the British harbour was to be planted. He had spent his holidays there and was completely conversant, not only with the coast, but the state of the tide and formations of the sea-bed. The information which he produced was of the greatest value when the landing took place.
>
> The combined report had, in the first instance, to be presented to Admiral Badger, of the US Navy, who was the Chairman of the committee dealing with supplies for all theatres of war. I had met the Admiral at Quebec and although he was friendly I realised he had some grievance which I was determined to elucidate. Admiral Badger asked me to bring a preliminary copy of the report in order that he should be briefed before the meeting. He then took a step almost without precedent by asking me to attend this meeting in order to put the case to the other

9

members of his committee. The result was highly successful and the
committee passed the report in all its stages.

I then sought out the Hon. Reggie Winn, ADC to Field Marshal Sir
John Dill, who was the Chief British representative on the Combined
Chiefs of Staffs. I had known Dill for many years. He was on the
divisional staff as a Junior Officer of the 55th Division, with which we had
both served during the First War. In addition, I found another old friend,
General Sir. G. Macready, who had served in the same Division and was
on the Combined Staff in Washington. He arranged that Brigadier Bruce
White, representing the War Office, and myself should attend the
Combined Chiefs of Staffs meeting when the final decision was made,
and a film which had been prepared in England was shown in order to
demonstrate some of the equipment. The plan was passed and, from my
point of view, the work in Washington was completed. Before leaving, I
was asked to bring the delegation to the White House in order to see the
Prime Minister. Having forced our way through the phalanx of detectives
who protected the White House, we were received by the Prime Minister
at 11 a.m. He was in bed smoking a large cigar. Some of the delegates
were rather nervous and so dropped their voices when talking to the
Prime Minister. As he [was] rather deaf, he failed to hear some of the
remarks and became rather ill-tempered, not wishing to confess that he
could not hear all that was said.

On the following Friday, President Roosevelt sent for the delegation,
but as I had arranged to go to New York for twenty-four hours before
proceeding to Montreal to catch the plane home, it was therefore, with
reluctance, I declined. This turned out to be fortunate because, if I had
caught the same train on the following day, I should have been involved
in a very severe railway accident which caused a number of casualties.

The return journey was uneventful; immediately on arrival I took up
my new quarters in Norfolk House, and started on the main problem
which lay before me.

It was at the meetings of the Combined Chiefs of Staff in Quebec and immediately
afterwards in Washington, that the final agreement for the construction of artificial
harbours was reached, and the codename 'Mulberry' accepted. Sir Bruce White
explains precisely how this codename came to be used.

Shortly after my return from top-secret meetings in North America
during August and September 1943, which were concerned with planning
Operation Overlord, the Allied invasion of Europe, I found on my desk at
the War Office a letter from a senior officer. The letter had no cover of
secrecy and was headed simply 'ARTIFICIAL HARBOURS'. This
breach of security appalled me. Fearful that such a letter could reveal a
most important secret, in the wrong hands, I immediately sought an

interview with the head of security at the War Office. I insisted that the project be given a code name. During the interview the security chief turned to a young officer behind him and asked for the next code word appearing on the list. The officer consulted a large volume and announced the word 'Mulberry', which I accepted. At the time we were already using 'Gooseberry' and 'Whale' but had I been offered 'Raspberry' I should not have accepted! This was the name adopted for the project and so it has remained to this day. Numerous myths have grown up about the origin of the code name but this is the actual story of how it came about.

'Artificial Harbours' were now concealed behind the accepted codename, but the logistics of how, where, and by whom they should be constructed, paid-for, and transported, still remained to be considered. This was the main problem which still lay before Sir Harold Wernher, and before the War Office represented by Sir Bruce White. Sir Bruce provides a general idea of the magnitude of the task ahead.

Harbour engineering is always a lengthy business but in the circumstances it was clear that ways and means would have to be found, by the fullest use of originality and improvisation, to provide special equipment and techniques to shorten the period of construction of all our responsibilities.

The organisation, therefore, was a specially selected staff of engineers at the War Office to deal with the many facets of harbour engineering, both for control and design. For their operation, a large force of Royal Engineers (REs) — again officered by experts — was built up and formed into various companies. Among these companies were Port Construction and Repair, Port Operating, Port Maintenance, Repair Shops, Dredging and Inland Waterways.

The force eventually reached a total of 1,332 officers and 51,740 men. They served in the ports, harbours and beaches of every theatre of war. I am pleased to place on record that, in the whole of the military forces employed within this group, the officers were all civilians who joined for particular duties.

The design proper was not actually started until October 1943, although much preparatory work and testing behind the scenes had been done since Sir Winston Churchill's memorandum 'PIERS FOR USE ON BEACHES' of May 1942 to the Chief of Combined Operations, of which group I was a member. The actual invasion was planned for May 1944.

Following the Quebec Conference, only eight months remained to achieve an engineering accomplishment never previously matched, nor equalled since.

I have already related how it was necessary to create a register of engineers, particularly those who had an experience of port engineering. At the time, many were either in one of the services or ministries, or still in civilian life. From this register a team of about 150 specialist engineers was formed but the Treasury, while seeing the importance of such a body, insisted that a loan should pay for the fees of such specialists and their staff. As the availability of such men was required quickly I put it to the Treasury that paying them at once out of a 'float' was the only practicable method.

The Treasury finally acquiesced and this float became renewable, subject to the provision of receipts.

At an exhibition of the models of the invasion harbours given later for the benefit of the Houses of Parliament, Lord Lloyd George — son of the First World War Prime Minister — enquired about the organisation for Mulberry. When I explained about its financing he said that no-one had ever succeeded in obtaining from the Treasury a continuous 'float' out of which fees for specialist civilian engineers were paid and there was no precedent for such a method of payment. He told me, 'you are the only man to have achieved this'.

In addition to the register of engineers, consulting engineering firms were engaged to supervise the many contracts being carried out in various parts of the United Kingdom.

Such an organisation was essential to complete the various works in a specified time. In advance of D-day the artificial harbours, having been built, had to be towed 100 miles to their destinations at about the same time as the assault troops, to enable them to be established in position, albeit 'under fire'.

Absolute secrecy had to be maintained about the operation. In order to maintain it this great engineering complex was divided into separate parts, particularly for the manufactured items. Orders for supply were placed with numerous firms — about 500 in all — spread throughout Britain. The manufactured items were brought together as near as possible to the date of the invasion.

Nearly all personnel had to be kept in complete ignorance of the purpose of the components and their eventual use.

The maintenance of security of this nature was in itself a great burden of responsibility, particularly when added to the other strains must be carried in a project of this magnitude.

Sir Harold Wernher explains the design of the harbours, and lists the component parts of each harbour, which explains Sir Bruce's reference to 'magnitude'.

The following comprised the main constructions:
   —   An outer breakwater of floating steel structures called
       Bombardons, anchored in the open sea in two rows with 400
       yards interval between them and lying parallel with and
       seaward of the Phoenix.

12

- An inner main breakwater of concrete caissons called *Phoenix* in the deep water.
- And a breakwater consisting of sunken block ships called *Gooseberry*.
- Inside the breakwater or harbour, a number of piers — six USA and nine British — floating up and down on the tide called *Whales* these being connected with the mainland by flexible floating roadways. Each of these was divided into sections or spans of 480 ft. for towing purposes.

As with Sir Bruce White, Sir Harold Wernher had also made contingency plans for organising construction, personnel and deployment of supplies, in the firm hope that the Mulberry proposal would be accepted by the Combined Chiefs of Staff, as indeed proved to be the case. He explains what he had already set in motion by the summer of 1943.

> Before leaving for Quebec, I had been fortunate in obtaining, through Sir Andrew Duncan, the Minister of Supply, the services of my old friend Jack Gibson. He was to be in charge of the constructional side of the production of the *Phoenix*. A Yorkshire man, he had started life contracting for Pearson & Co., and later, when the first Lord Cowdray retired from the business, he had made Gibson a present of over £100,000 worth of plant in gratitude for his services. With this plant Gibson had carried out some big contracts in Lower Egypt and the Sudan. The remaining work, such as pierheads, flexible floating roadways, pontoons, etc., were handled by Mr R A Davis, an employee of Vauxhall lent to the Ministry of Supply. I was to have the most happy relations with these two capable men and it is doubtful whether two better selections could have been made for the purpose.
>
> At the same time it was necessary for me to have liaison with the Admiralty and the Americans. Before leaving for Quebec, Vice Admiral Sir Frederic Wake-Walker, the Controller, had appointed Captain, later Vice Admiral Hickling, RN, as liaison officer with the Admiralty. Hickling came to see me and asked what his duties would be. I informed him that I could give him no details for some days and suggested that he should immediately take ten day's leave, because he had been on service without leave for many months. This was a fortunate proposal, because I think that, as a result of this, we became firm friends from the start. At the same time General Lee, at my request, appointed Brigadier-General H B Vaughan, an officer in the Corps of Engineers, to represent the American interests. Vaughan was a very able and experienced officer, having been in charge of many public works during the time when unemployment was rife in the USA and the unemployed were being used for large constructional schemes, such as damming the Mississippi,

[constructing] airfields, roads, etc. He therefore had a great knowledge of the work which lay before us. Subsequently, when he was appointed Major General, he delegated the day-to-day work to his assistant, Colonel C M Spainhour, of the US Corps of Engineers. The latter had a charming personality and a great capacity for putting his finger on the weak spots. In addition, I had my able assistant Colonel T B Bunting. I was therefore fortunate in having collected a team of really first-class men who were not only loyal, but had no feelings other than getting on with the job.

During my absence in the USA Bunting had been engaged in a preliminary survey of all the work in connection with the Mulberry project. When I returned, I found that he had already made the necessary contacts with the Admiralty, War Office and Ministries of Production and Supply, and had prepared a report embodying all the work carried out, thus saving me a great deal of intricate detail, for which I was greatly relieved.

The first important action to be taken before leaving for Quebec, was to mobilise the labour required. I had had an interview with Sir Godfrey Ince at the Ministry of Labour, and warned him that we should require more than 10,000 men from the building trade by the end of September. I also suggested the consideration of the employment of Italian prisoners if labour was not forthcoming from existing sources. Meanwhile the War Office were producing some 230 drawings for the *Phoenix*, but when they were presented to the Contractors in October, the design was complicated and would have caused endless delays in production. I therefore consulted the Controller of the Admiralty and he brought in Dr. Oscar Faber, an expert in concrete, who submitted modifications, many of which were embodied in the final design. Eventually 142 alterations in the designs were needed.

I had frequent meetings with Admiral Wake-Walker on the question of labour and supplies. I was told that one of his peculiarities was, if he disagreed, to take off his spectacles, poise them in the air and then, if he threw them on to the table, it was quite certain he would not yield to any suggestions made to him. It was therefore with consternation that I noted, after I had asked him a very leading question, he started to adopt the procedure which I knew would be fatal. So, as his hand was raised to dash the spectacles on to the table, I seized him by the arm, saying, 'Admiral, you must not throw down your spectacles, otherwise you will not agree to my proposals'. Whereupon he laughed and, after about half-an-hour's argument, agreed to carry out all my suggestions.

The procedure for the next months was that Gibson would either see me or telephone me every morning with his requirements and I would endeavour to meet the demands.

14

Sir Bruce White, on his return from the Quebec Conference, was appalled by the tight schedule for the completion of the project, as, unlike Sir Harold, he had received no earlier intimations of the precise scale of the construction work. He was also required to find suitable sites where it could best be carried out.

On my return to Britain, the commitment weighed more heavily. The most important item to be concentrated on within the short time available was the provision of 150 concrete 'caissons' weighing 7,000 tons each to form breakwaters. I immediately contacted Sir Andrew Duncan, the Cabinet minister with responsibility for supply.

At a meeting at 8 a.m. at Steel House in Tothill Street the minister asked what was wanted. I explained to him the mission to North America and the extreme secrecy attending the discussions and their great purpose. I said that it would now be necessary to set up a new organisation for dealing with the supply of concrete which had not previously been catered for. Sir Andrew asked what form this new department should take. I told him that it would now be necessary, among other things, that large numbers of contractors should be coordinated by an experienced engineer on the staff of his ministry. By the same afternoon, the appointment was made.

The production of the 150 concrete caissons required the allocation of a large number of building sites at which accommodation for the work force was available, as well as roads and railways and office accommodation. In addition, facilities had to be found for the consulting engineering firms responsible for supervising the work.

One such site was Stokes Bay, Gosport, Hampshire where the caissons formed on the promenade were advanced sideways across the slipway into the sea. The East India Dock in London was dewatered for the construction of caissons and flooded to float them into the River Thames.

My greatest disappointment in finding sites was at Southampton, where the King George V Dock had been allotted to me and in which at least ten caissons could have been built. Unfortunately, the Admiralty stepped in and claimed the dock for the manufacture of their steel alternative to our concrete caissons, named Bombardons, although these could easily have been built on a beach and rolled into the sea.

I established several working committees to progress the development of Mulberry. One of these became known as the Artificial Harbours Committee and met at Montague House. In addition, two civilian committees were established, the Caisson Design Committee and the Contractor's Committee. These committees reported to me through my deputy, Colonel (later Brigadier) Rolfe.

By December 1943, with the assistance of Mr Ernest Bevin, the Minister of Labour, we had recruited over 25,000 men who were deployed at various locations throughout the country for the construction of the Mulberry harbours. Altogether, some 300 firms were involved in the construction of the pierheads, to which ships would moor for unloading, and a further 250 were making the floating roadways to carry the vehicles onto the beaches. None of these contractors had drawings of the complete scheme and complete security was maintained.

By this stage, with the War Office, the Government, the Civil Service, the Army and both the British and American navies involved in the preparation of Mulberry, it was necessary to allocate responsibilities to each department or service to ensure the smoothest possible co-operation. Hints of difficulty had already emerged at the Quebec Conference, when Sir Harold Wernher found Admiral King of the US Navy both reluctant to co-operate, and, eventually, less than generous in the quality of the tugs which he provided.

Vice Admiral Hickling saw, early on, both the need for sensible divisions of responsibilities, and some of the difficulties inherent in making such a division. He explains

> In so novel a project it was inevitable that there should be considerable doubt at the outset as to who was to do what. In the very early days I do not think that the Navy fully realised the immensity of the task nor the very large part which they would have to play. 'Transportation' at the War Office, with Brigadier Bruce White and Colonel Steer Webster in the van, were much more alive to the various problems. After a lot of back-chat , it was decided broadly that the Navy should be responsible for the Bombardons and blockships, assembling of all parts of the harbour on the South side of the United Kingdom, and for towing them across the Channel and constructing the breakwaters, while the Army should be responsible for the construction of Phoenix and Whale, and for the erection of the Whale piers on the far shore; also for the technical side of the Phoenix, such as opening the sinking valves.
>
> Although there was some bickering in Whitehall, once we got down to the coast everyone worked in very well together. Soldiers, sailors, (RN and MN) — British and Americans; Ministry of War Transport; Ministry of Supply; Sappers, Sea Bees; tug men; local authorities — they all had but one object, to get ready in time for D-day. That object was achieved with about ten minutes to spare!

Sir Bruce White's words echo Vice Admiral Hickling's estimate of his awareness of the need to divide responsibilities.

> It was clear in the early days that an operation involving the invasion of the Continent should be vested in combined operations of the forces, namely the Royal Navy, the War Office, and the Air Force. I represented the War Office at meetings of Combined Operations under Lord Mountbatten to discuss invasion plans.

What, however, at that early stage of planning, had not become clear was that the functions of each of the Services and Departments in the overall plan inevitably over-lapped with those of the others, which, at times was to cause considerable friction. For example, when he returned from the Quebec Conference in August 1943, Sir Bruce White appeared to have understood from the information received at that Conference, that he was in complete charge of the actual construction of Mulberry. He said

> So far as the organisation which was built up, this consisted of direction by myself with a deputy, with a great number of properly qualified people with delegated responsibility. The latter were trained as military officers because, although in the early stages they would be responsible for design, ultimately these men would be sent overseas with the forces.
>
> The greatest possible use was made of consulting engineers and other specialists. Many committees were formed consisting of experts acting in an advisory capacity to ensure the success of every branch of our activities.

But, from some time before the Quebec Conference took place, Major General Wernher appears to have been selected as director of the organisation, and before he went to Canada, he had already implemented some preliminary plans. He explains:

> At the beginning of August, a month after the Largs Conference, the P.A.O. Committee recommended that I should be appointed the Chief Co-ordinator for the Mulberry project. Although the plans were in a very preliminary state, I immediately visited the Minister of Production, the Rt. Hon. Oliver Lyttleton, who called several of his executives together to meet me. I explained the problem and warned them of the vast quantities of steel and other supplies which would be required if the Mulberry project was approved at the Quebec Conference. I immediately found an attitude of co-operation and was able to place certain preliminary orders in advance of the official sanction.

At this point, Sir Bruce saw himself as 'Director', and Sir Harold as 'Chief Co-ordinator' of the Mulberry project. To a layman, it is not easy to define the precise distinction between the two rôles. It is possible that certain of the tensions which arose at this point and persisted almost throughout the project amongst the War Office and the Services, including both British and American personnel, might have been considerably eased had each department been aware of the exact bounds defining its operation. This, however, considering the size of the endeavour, might well have been almost impossible, and it is remarkable how, in the end, most leaders and most Services worked together.

Exact demarcations of authority did, nevertheless, sometimes lead to acrimonious divisions of opinion. Sir Harold Wernher gives an account of one such incident between Sir Bruce White and the Admiralty, which caused a great deal of ill feeling before it was resolved.

As the construction proceeded, Vice Admiral Tennant, later Sir William Tennant, was brought in to COSSAC in order to plan the movement and erection of the *Mulberry* harbour on the site. Captain Hickling joined his staff, although he was continually in touch with me. The main difficulty Admiral Tennant had to face was that all the equipment had been ordered on a plan drawn up by the War Office. It would be impossible to accelerate the production, in fact it was doubtful if it would even be finished by May 1st, and therefore he had to make do with the equipment which was put in hand during September. During the winter, a crisis arose between the War Office and the Admiralty. Brigadier Bruce White, who was responsible for the original design of the *Phoenix* could not appreciate that, once they were manufactured and floating, they came under the Admiralty, being classified at this stage as ships. The situation got so serious that the Controller refused to see Bruce White and would only deal with me. Eventually I had to take the matter up with General Morgan. He summoned a meeting, but unfortunately had a very bad cold and could not contribute with his usual efficiency, with the result that the matter was referred to the Chiefs of Staff. At this time the Chiefs of Staff were at the Teheran Conference and their deputies had been told to produce a memorandum over the week-end, and, after it had been discussed, Nye turned to me and said that this was not a matter for the Chiefs of Staff, and that if I was a Co-ordinator, why did I not co-ordinate? To which I replied that one could not co-ordinate if people did not wish to be co-ordinated. Whereupon Admiral Sir Bertie Ramsay entered the discussion wholeheartedly on my side and eventually, after a very acrimonious argument, the matter was referred back to General Morgan and, as we all thought, settled.

I went to the Admiralty and agreed with the staff of the First Sea Lord, Sir Andrew Cunningham, the form which the directive should take, but in a subsequent meeting of the Chiefs of Staff, Cunningham, who had not been present at the first occasion, altered the directive and therefore put me in an extremely difficult position. I accordingly went to see him personally. When I arrived, the Admiral was in a very bad temper, because on the previous evening a bomb had dropped on Whitehall and he had had to take cover under his desk; all the windows in his office were blown in. In addition, there had been some misunderstanding between the Royal Navy and the US navy with regard to the patrolling of the Bay of Biscay area, with the result that a contraband ship had escaped from Spain and reached Le Havre. I therefore had to listen to a tale of woe for some half hour, but finally we discussed the directive and the Admiral agreed to put it forward in its original form.

Bruce White was determined to continue to fight against the Admiralty, and I received a letter signed by him on behalf of Lt. General McMullen, the Director of Transportation, insinuating that the work would never be finished in time and that the blame for this must be placed upon me. I immediately decided that this was an issue of such importance that it must be taken to the highest level, which would probably have meant the end of Bruce White. However, I recollected a story told to me by Prince Louis of Battenberg, later the first Marquess of Milford Haven and the father of Admiral Mountbatten, when he was First Lord. Prince Louis had inspected a Naval establishment and had found fault. The following morning he received an insubordinate letter from the Admiral concerned. As Prince Louis had the greatest admiration for the Officer, he wrote to him saying that he had to acknowledge his letter of such-and-such a date, which he had not read, and that he returned the letter herewith. I rang up General McMullen and told him that he must withdraw the letter and I also told him this story, whereupon I sent him back the letter and the incident was closed.

Vice Admiral Hickling, as might have been expected, took the part of the Navy in the dispute over the control of testing of the Phoenix, and makes it more explicit than the more under-stated account given by Sir Harold.

To be wise after the event, I think it would have been better if the Navy instead of the Army had undertaken the Phoenixes; as I have said they were concrete ships or hulks and, whereas it is part of naval routine to accept ships when they leave the builder's hands to carry out equipment trials, handling trials and so forth, such things naturally are not provided for in the War Office. Amateurs, however enthusiastic and with the best advice in the world, cannot have the same knowledge and experience as those who have made seafaring their profession. As it was, when D-day approached, the Navy took over the equipment of the Phoenixes and prepared them for the passage across the Channel.

Hickling, then only Captain Hickling, was in no doubt that Sir Harold Wernher's task as Co-ordinator was exceedingly complex, and he remained certain that no-one could have succeeded better. He explains

The co-ordination of all the various authorities and Ministries concerned in this vast building programme was a formidable task. The Phoenixes employed twenty-five contractors and 20,000 men in prefabricating the best part of a million tons of reinforced concrete. There were 240 different firms in the United Kingdom concerned with the 50,000 tons of highly-specialized steel work of the Whale; the parts of the 115 Bombardons had to be taken from all over the kingdom to be assembled — twenty every three weeks — in the King George V dock at Southampton. This task of co-ordinating the Admiralty, the War Office, Ministries of War Transport, of Supply, of Production, and of Labour — to mention but a few of the parties concerned, fell to General Sir Harold Wernher. He was also responsible for the Hards over which the assault loaded up for D-day. With a single assistant, Colonel Bunting, and a military and a naval liaison officer — Colonel Dadly and myself — he carried out a very difficult job in a most able fashion. Above all he kept the peace between the more irascible members and reconciled the often conflicting interests and priorities.

I think it is fair to say that in those early days we found no difficulty in getting a straight answer out of the Admiralty — often a very straight one from the Controller when we cast covetous eyes on his docks or the steel for his frigates; but Rear Admiral Patterson and Commander Peters got us everything we asked for.

Sir Jack Gibson, the master contractor on the Phoenixes, acting for the Ministry of Supply, was a tower of strength and was always as good as his word.

With our friends on the other side of Whitehall it was not so easy to get down to brass tacks — we never seemed to be able to find one individual, except Colonel Steer-Webster, who could speak with full authority and give quick decisions.

As the construction stage gave way to the operational stage, *i.e.*, the assembly and the operation itself, so the burden of co-ordination passed from Sir Harold Wernher as CM & SF (Co-ordinator of Ministries and Services Facilities) to Rear Admiral William Tennant, RAMP, (Rear Admiral Mulberry and Pluto.) It was on 3rd January, 1944, that Admiral Ramsay made Tennant directly responsible for both Mulberries and Pluto, with me as his Chief of Staff.

General Wernher's skills as a go-between and a pourer of oil on waters which sometimes seemed as troubled as they were to become, in fact, during the great storm of June 19th 1944, did not prevent him from allocating blame when he thought this was justified. He was also very firm in supporting those whom he thought had been treated with less than justice, as the following anecdote indicates.

Amongst the sites selected for the construction of the *Phoenix* was Stokes Bay, near Portsmouth. The contractor for this area came to me with a grievance, for his most important engineer had been forbidden by the Admiralty to work in the area. I discovered that he was the son of Kerensky, the initiator of the Russian Revolution in 1917. After considerable argument with the C-in-C Portsmouth, I persuaded him to withdraw the ban and Kerensky continued to function throughout the construction period.

This particular site was immediately adjacent to an area which had been selected by Major-General Sir Percy Hobart, an eminent tank expert, for experiments in connection with a very secret floating tank. The General made his objections to the C-in-C Home Forces, General Paget, and stated that, for security reasons, he could not permit the constructional operations to continue in Stokes Bay.

General Paget, being unable to settle the question, sent Hobart to see me. I knew him to be a very decisive person, but being unable to move him, I pointed out that it was useless for him to dispute the case because I would, if necessary, obtain an over-ruling authority. This, of course, I had to do, but General Hobart and I remained very good friends in spite of it and no leakage of security resulted.

Kerensky justified the trust which Wernher had reposed in him, 'no leakage of security resulted'. His engineering skills were not wasted and the construction of the Phoenix at Stokes Bay was not interrupted. In other cases, Sir Harold was not prepared to gloss over what he felt had been indecisiveness and errors of judgement. He later said that amongst the chief lessons learnt from Mulberry were:

(a) Frequent alteration of plans and drawings must at all costs be avoided. The tendency to improve and add to the design while understandable must be resisted; finality must be reached at the earliest possible moment. For *Phoenix* alone, 142 alterations or additions were made. If these alterations could have been avoided, the original target date would have been met.

It is impossible to undertake detailed planning of an inter-Service project when one of the Services is not represented by the user. Delay in appointing technical Transportation Officers to 21 Army Group, led to most unfortunate hold-ups which resulted in last minute demands that were difficult to meet.

The War Office accepted the responsibility for assembly of the roadways and pierheads without having the necessary skilled direction or labour for the task. It was necessary to call upon the Ministry of Supply and the American Navy for assistance at the last minute. Such work should be undertaken by those with the necessary production experience.

He tactfully names no names. From the accounts of others whose experiences are described in this book, some of them can very easily be deduced. In the end, however, General Wernher's desire for just recognition for all those whose work had been of service to the final success of Mulberry, caused him to speak more plainly. This came about when the Press published a very partial account of the operation.

Between October 16th and 23rd, 1944, all the newspapers published the story of Mulberry, together with photographs and a full description of the work that had been undertaken. The following morning I received a number of telephone calls from those who had been associated with me, complaining that several of those who had contributed largely to the success had not been mentioned in any account. They were also indignant that no mention had been made of myself. I accordingly read all the newspapers concerned and found this was correct.

I then wrote to General Morgan pointing out this fact, and asking if there was any particular reason for the omission. I drew his attention to the controversies which had arisen with the War Office during the last months and said I presumed they had issued the *communiqué*, and, in view of this, had purposely excluded mention of my name and that of several others who had assisted me. General Morgan replied that he had been greatly disturbed that no mention had been made, and stated that when he had held a Press Conference originally, he had not given any special mention to myself as it was 'common knowledge' that I was one of the prime movers. He stated that he would interview the Public Relations Department and see if anything could be done to rectify the error. I replied to General Morgan pointing out that the security measures we had taken had been highly successful, and for this reason my association with the venture could, in no sense, have been 'common knowledge', and in a recent *communiqué* all the names had been mentioned of those who had been working under me. Although General Morgan promised to make a further move in the matter, I never heard anything more from him.

At about the same time I received a letter from Admiral Mountbatten complaining that Combined Operations, which had initiated the idea *of* Mulberry harbours, under Captain Hughes-Hallett and Captain Hussey, had also been excluded from any mention. He presumed that this was owing to the jealousy of the other Services towards Combined Operations. He also stated that he had put my name forward for recognition and had spoken to the King on the question.

As was stated earlier, the drawings and designs were actually prepared by the War Office, under Brigadier Bruce White, who received a KBE for his part in the project.

Bruce White was an extremely good looking man, in fact his colleagues stated that this was one of the reasons which had prevented him from becoming an engineer. He was not *persona grata* with the Contractors because, it was said, by training he was an electrical engineer, whereas this task was one for a constructional engineer.

Furthermore, he was continually endeavouring to side-track the Admiralty and, insofar as the design was concerned, when it was proved to him by experts that this was in many respects faulty (in fact they refused to accept responsibility for his specifications), instead of admitting this, he endeavoured to cover it up by every kind of device. There was no question, therefore, that, in view of the difficulty I had with him and his department, he was determined to take the full credit to himself.

When I had completed my task, I received letters from all those who had been associated with me, congratulating me on the work done and thanking me for the very tactful way I had handled the many difficult problems. I refer particularly to a letter from the Controller, Admiral Wake-Walker, in which he said he knew I would like to know how much he appreciated my 'tactful work', which had smoothed over all the differences inevitable in such a venture. I received similar letters from other members of the Naval Staff at the Admiralty. I also received a personal letter from General Lee of the United States Army in similar terms to that of the Controller, and from Admiral Ramsay and Admiral Tennant, with whom I had been in close contact throughout. Mr Bevin made the following statement to Admiral Mountbatten, 'You certainly put the right man in charge of getting the *Mulberry* finished, because Wernher was not afraid to come to see me when all other means of getting labour failed, and I was glad to be able to help him'.

Meanwhile Admiral Mountbatten was still pursuing the topic of recognition and wrote to General Brownjohn who, in his reply, stated 'The fact that the *Phoenix* was ready by D-day was due, in my opinion, very largely to Wernher's efforts, but I do not think that this will ever be recognised, except by the few who knew. He made too many enemies in official circles by his forceful methods'.

Admiral Mountbatten subsequently learnt from the War Office that I was recommended for an award, but that Grigg (then Secretary of State for War) personally scratched it out after it had passed through every Committee, saying that, so long as he was in office, he would never pass my name.

The above is described to indicate the petty jealousy and short-sightedness of certain people in authority who appeared to be more intent on defeating each other than the common enemy!

This account, written after the event, serves to highlight the problems, difficulties, and personal animosities which might, had they remained unsolved, unresolved and unreconciled, have made it impossible to complete Mulberry at all, let alone complete it in such a short time.

Now, returning to 1942, the designs had been made, personnel assembled, sites chosen. The decision and planning stage was complete. Execution was to follow.

GROWING PAINS

In the autumn of 1942, Tn5 received a Mulberry specification from Combined Operations Headquarters, which at that time was headed by Mountbatten. The specification required 'a pierhead capable of berthing three 2000 ton vessels simultaneously, and a pier which would allow continuous traffic flow over a length of not less than one mile'. In January 1943, Tn5 formed a Royal Engineer unit — No. 1 Transportation Fixed and Floating Equipment Development and Training Depot. This cumbersomely titled unit, under the command of Major J G Carline, was to be responsible for development of and training in use of what became Mulberry Piers. Tn5 was given the task of evaluating the three designs that had been submitted against the specification. It was around this time that Scotland entered the Mulberry story, as one of the first requirements was to locate a suitable development area, as Sir Bruce White recalls.

> It was necessary to test the components for the artificial harbours. I tried out any proposal, whether it was made by my own staff, by another Service or even by individuals. A testing site had to be found in the UK for these trials. A search of various areas resulted in the selection of a location in the Solway Firth where the rise and fall of the tide — about 24 feet — was similar to that off Normandy. It was also subject, at times, to very rough seas. Above all, however, its remoteness from London decided the issue, as interested visitors were reduced to the minimum. Police protection was provided, when I approached the Scottish authorities, and a small unit was established at the experimental site.

The chosen site was that part of the Solway Firth around the small fishing village of Garlieston in Wigtownshire. As a result of Bruce White's interest the harbour was sealed off by barbed wire from the rest of the world, and the harbour and nearby Rigg Bay were closed to the public. A direct telephone line from the harbour to the War Office in London was installed.

Security was vital, and that it remained tight throughout the whole of the testing and construction period can be in no doubt. It is extraordinary that, considering the thousands of workers eventually involved in Mulberry construction, the enemy had no idea of what was taking place.

A story persists of an MI5 agent[1] who, in the guise of a tramp, visited the area to test security. Ensconced in the Galloway Arms he was spotted by Major Carline who

---

[1] This story is possibly apocryphal since it is questionable whether or not an unknown tramp would have progressed beyond the security cordon surrounding Garlieston village. Nonetheless, when visiting the War Office when the war was over, a colleague informed Major Carline that an officer wished to return his hospitality and he was approached by a colonel with whom he was unfamiliar. 'You once treated me to a drink,' declared the latter. The unknown colonel was, in fact, the Garlieston 'tramp'.

ordered the publican to give him a pint. The security of the locals proved first rate and the MI5 officer was unable to glean anything of what was afoot in Garlieston. In 1995 Miss Jean Hill of Baltier Farm, then in her eighties, related an intriguing story about security provisions in Garlieston.

On the decision to site the top-secret trials of the prototype Mulberry units at Garlieston, Rigg Bay and Portyerrock Bay, my father Capt. Peter Hill was contacted by the War Office regarding security matters and subsequently put in charge, with a direct telephone line to the War Office. He was a retired sea captain who also had been an assessor for Lloyds.

The highest point on Baltier Farm is Gallows Hill from where one has a clear view of Rigg and Portyerrock Bays and the outer bay at Garlieston. It also had an uninterrupted view of all other vantage points that overlook the area where the proposed Mulberry activity was to take place and where any enemy agent would be likely to place himself. A stone dyke [wall] facing on to these areas was taken down and replaced by an imitation dyke complete with little windows, which allowed a hidden observer to view and monitor the whole area. A private telephone line ran from this observation hut to Baltier farmhouse where, secreted in a small bedside cabinet, my father had his direct line to the War Office. When any lights were visible beyond but near the Mulberry sites, father, a morse-code expert, was alerted to read any messages that were transmitted, and relay them direct to the War Office. He also had a specially wide stool constructed which stood by his bedroom window so he could stand on it to overlook the bay.

To help man this post, a man was sent from the Secret Service in London, and stayed with us and was suitably fitted out in old worn working clothes. His cover included working in the farm garden, and every now and then he would take a horse and cart to deliver something or other to another farm, taking the opportunity to gossip with passers-by or any locals he met. In reality he was gathering information regarding movements of strangers and testing the knowledge that had been gained by the locals concerning the goings-on. To further assist in the manning of the observation hut, another undercover man, who lived at Portyerrock Farm was Captain Black, a retired sea captain. These two were augmented by my brother James, who farmed Baltier; as well as two other farmers, Bill Brown of Cutreoch, Isle of Whithorn, and John Wallace of Whitehills, Sorbie. At times of unforeseen events on the farm, father would delegate me to man the post while my brother sorted out the problem. The Home Guard under John Wyllie of Wyllie's Mill in Garlieston, much to their chagrin, were not allowed to have anything to do with it, and so for 50 years this story was never told.

One of my lighter memories concerns the arrival of a top man from the War Office who wished to view all the activity without being seen, so my brother and I had to induce John Owen, the butcher in Garlieston, to lend us some of his old, worn and patched clothes. Thus decked out, our man from the War Office was set on the top of a cartload of straw and sent to deliver it to Bill Brown at Cutreoch and other farms, thereby giving him a leisurely insight as to how the work was progressing and the security arrangements at Portyerrock Bay — that was of course as long as the horse did not bolt!

The target date for the Solway trials was to be sometime in March, 1943. The importance of the time, and the momentum behind the scheme, is well expressed by Allan Beckett in the following extract.

Perhaps as a result of this [Churchill's] directive, Everall, on returning from one of his visits to the War Office, produced a sketch marked 'Top Secret' and asked me whether, as a keen sailor, I could make sense of it.

The sketch showed a mile-long series of pontoons, each with four legs looking like four-poster beds, and linked by bridges which overall covered a stretch of water shallow at one end and deep at the other. The caption was 'Piers for flat beaches' — and that was all. There was no explanation, though by scaling the sketch it could be found that the spacing of the pontoons was about 80 feet.

My reaction was that the pontoons and legs were an unnecessary complication for a floating bridge, and that the same objective could be reached by a more conventional system — as long as it was designed to accept the sea action without overstress — and I said as much.

Everall said 'If you think you know how to do better you must make it clear before next Monday when I shall be visiting the War Office'. With the help of Sgt. Major Gaunt, who was skilled with the soldering iron, I made a tin plate model of my proposed flexible floating roadway. It consisted of one torsion-free lozenge shaped bridge span and part of an adjacent span to show how the span-to-span junction could be made using spherical bearings.

When Everall returned he was on top of the world. 'Beckett' he said, 'they want six spans built right away and I have promised that you will produce the works drawings by the end of the week!'

The order for the prototype bridge spans was placed with Messrs Braithwaite of West Bromwich and a test site was established at Cairn Head near Garlieston in Scotland. For the pontoons to support the bridge spans I suggested an adaptation of Thames lighters, and this was done for the prototypes, though I was well aware that there would not be sufficient lighters available if this scheme did go ahead.

The War Office enthusiasm for the floating bridge seemed to intensify, and Everall was instructed to bring his whole design team to London. This he did and we were accommodated in County Hall and given the title of 'Tn5' in the department of Docks and Inland Water Transportation. I was appointed Deputy Assistant Director with Staff Major rank.

The pierhead and bridge design described above was in fact the last of the prototypes to be tested. The first scheme was proposed by consulting engineer Iorys Hughes, a Welshman, designer of the Empire swimming pool at Wembley and a well-known yachtsman. His design consisted of a fixed pier and pierhead with two main components. The first was a large concrete caisson, 200 feet long and 45 feet wide. Codenamed 'Hippo'; this was to support the second component, steel spans codenamed 'Crocodiles' that, when positioned on sunken Hippos, would form a roadway. Bruce White arranged construction of prototype caissons at Holloway Bros. Ltd. As no dry dock was available, a site was found on a golf course at Conway, North Wales, adjacent to the tidal estuary of the River Conway. Three Hippos weighing 3,200 tons each were built simultaneously. A steel superstructure was added and in June 1943 they were launched sideways down a slipway. In July they were towed to Rigg Bay, Garlieston; and all had arrived by early August, and by mid August the Hippos had been positioned offshore. A floating crane added linking Crocodiles.

Early indications were that Hughes' idea was not a winning one. The piers could not, as specified, move vertically with the tide and the Hippos were prone to scouring at the base which could have led to listing with disastrous results for any vehicles on the roadways at the time[2].

The second idea, nicknamed 'Swiss Roll' was proposed by Ronald Marsden Hamilton. He was a brilliant mathematician with a flair for inventing. He had a crippled right arm which, although it prevented him from joining the Royal Navy in WWI, did not appear to deter him from being an enthusiastic yachtsman, who volunteered to assist in the Dunkirk evacuation in 1940.

In February 1942, Hamilton came to the attention of the Royal Navy Directorate of Miscellaneous Weapon Development (DMWD). At that time he was working on 'Rolling Dynamic Buoyancy' from a laboratory in a bomb-damaged wing of the Grosvenor Hotel, London. Hamilton's idea was based on the Archimedean principle of displacement. Pictures of early prototypes showed his son riding a motorcycle, with passenger, across a wide stream supported only by fencing stakes laid over a tarpaulin — a truly floating roadway. Encouraged by his early successes, he had

---

[2] One of the Hippos can still be seen in Rigg Bay, its steel superstructure being a favourite haunt of cormorants. Also to be seen is a tapered stone base, 8 feet high, at the back of the beach at Rigg Bay. This was to be the landward end of a roadway brought ashore from the Hippos using Crocodiles. It was never used.

built a 200ft long tank from linoleum in one of the hotel corridors. Floating in the tank was a miniature roadway upon which was a model truck. This roadway differed from the early prototype in that the sides were hinged. As the truck moved along the roadway the sides flapped up under the weight of the vehicle to form a kerb that prevented the ingress of water. Once the vehicle had passed, the sides resumed their original position.

The Swiss Roll, like the Hughes Pier, was deemed unsuitable for the main purpose of Mulberry. It was, however, used during the invasion for offloading soldiers directly on to the beaches. During trials the Swiss Roll was responsible for some colourful, memorable and tragic incidents.

Willie Drynan, who still lives in Garlieston overlooking the harbour, remembers waking one morning to see soldiers walking on what he knew to be deep water. He shot out of bed and, to his amazement, saw that they were walking on a magic carpet. It was in fact a Swiss Roll that had arrived in barges the previous night, and had been unrolled in the early hours. Two lads from Whithorn, Willie Ballantyne and Johnny Mills, hoeing turnips at Portyerrock, were eating their lunch watching a truck going ashore across a Swiss Roll. One of them later said

> We decided we'd better say nocht aboot it when we got hame, because
> they wouldna believe us onyway, and we micht a' got a hidin'.

Archie McCallie still talks of the worst accident during the trials in Garlieston. His first job as a boy was at Callanders Sawmill, now the site of Garlieston Caravan Club site, and he saw a lot of what happened in the harbour. On one occasion a Hippo was moored at the entrance to the harbour with two Swiss Rolls laid end to end, reaching the road beside the village hall. A truck or jeep would drive along it on to a waiting Landing Craft (Tank). The LCT would then travel to Rigg Bay or Portyerrock Bay to off- load. Three cables ran the length of each roll. The landward end of the roll, which was joined to the other by a metal rod fitted through eyes, was moored to posts near the hall. The seaward end was attached to a tug which tensioned the whole roadway. One day Archie realised there was a stir on. Four soldiers rolling the end of the roll on the foreshore found the spring in the cables too much for them. The two on the outside jumped clear but the two who were left were drowned in the mud. By the time they were uncovered they were dead.

The third prototype, the 'spud' pierhead and floating roadway (Whale) was tested at Cairn Head. The 'spud' pontoon, which stood on four spud legs that could be raised and lowered by means of winches, was the key to its success. The pierhead for the Tn5 design was based on a dredger called *Lucayan*[3], designed in 1923 to work in the Bahamas and built by the Renfrew shipbuilding firm, Lobnitz & Co. Lobnitz had no difficulty in adapting their design for the purpose of Mulberry and was able to prepare new drawings in a matter of weeks. This meant that, from drawings

---

[3] This was the dredger in Valparaiso, referred to in Bruce White's account on page 6.

produced in December 1942, the prototype pierhead was ready and installed at Cairn Head by April 1943. At the time, it was the largest all welded waterbourne structure built in Scotland.

> The problem was one of, first of all, providing landing pontoons or pierheads, linking these all together by floating roadways, say anything up to one mile from the shore, and providing roadways from the pontoons themselves right to the shore. The problem was — how were these pontoons to be fixed in position so as to be a terminal for the bridge spans, and so that vessels could come alongside them unobstructed by any moorings.
>
> It was precisely the type of problem to which the Lobnitz organisation could bring to bear the necessary knowledge and enthusiasm. A prototype was designed by our engineering staff, without delay and just as soon as they were satisfied as to its workability, the steelwork of the construction was sub-contracted to Messrs. Findlay & Co., Ltd. of Motherwell. This prototype, although it was on paper only in December, 1942, was on its experimental station in the Solway Firth by April, 1943. A truly remarkable performance when it is considered that almost 1000 tons of steel were involved as well as the very heavy winches for operating the spuds with the attendant Diesel-electric gear and controls, all which mechanical portions we manufactured and fitted. This feat could never have been accomplished without the very close co-operation of all concerned and a very large measure of this achievement is due to the immense energy that was displayed by the late Mr P. W. Robson, then Chairman of Messrs Alex Findlay & Co. Ltd. This prototype was thoroughly tested in the Solway over a period of 13 months under the rigorous conditions of tide and storm encountered there and was found eminently satisfactory in every way. Approval was given to the wholesale construction of pierheads throughout the country [United Kingdom]. At these building sites, all the technical requirements involved were under the direct supervision of Lobnitz representatives. — *Shipbuilding and Shipping Record, February 22, 1945*

Although Lobnitz's achievement in getting the prototype on site in such a short time must be applauded, the work might yet have been completed even more quickly. Lt. H C McIntyre of the Royal Engineers was responsible for reporting on the progress of pierhead development. In the conclusion of one of his reports based on a visit to the Lobnitz works he writes:

> Throughout my tour of these factories I found that great surprise was shown in almost every case when I stressed the urgency of the work.
>
> Therefore I feel quite confident in saying that Messrs Lobnitz & Co., Ltd., had not taken full advantage of the priority allotted to this contract.

The spud pierhead or 'Whale' as it came to be known, was the first link in the vital ship-to-shore chain that would ensure the safe and effective delivery of supplies to the invasion beaches. It was a considerable piece of engineering. The following extract from Guy Hartcup's book *Code Name Mulberry* gives an idea of the pierhead's size and complexity:

> It had a very distinctive shape. At each end there were two high stacks like chimneys. These housed the spud legs which were no less than 89ft long with 4ft square. They were contained within guide frames enabling the spuds to slide up and down but giving great lateral stiffness. The spuds were operated by twin wire cables attached at one end to a 20hp electrically-operated winch with a reduction gear, and, at the other, to the top of the spud. The downhaul cable which passed over a sheave at the top of the spud lifted the hull by pressing the spud foot down on to the sea bed. The other cable passed over the lower end and was used for lifting the spud. The spuds could be raised or lowered at a rate of approximately 2½ft a minute. The winch motors were fitted with a magnetic brake which was set to hold a 12in lift of hull corresponding to a load of 84 tons on the spud. If this load was exceeded the brake automatically released the load to this figure. The motive power for the winches was provided by two 57kW diesels and generators, which also operated bollards, bilge pumps and other equipment. The other diesel was usually sufficient to operate the spuds; the second came into action when the weather demanded extra power.
>
> When floating with the spuds raised, the pontoon drew about 3ft 3in of water. When the spuds were lowered the draught was approximately 2ft 10in; the hull was then relieved of the weight of the spuds, each of which weighed some 35 tons. In calm weather the pontoon floated up and down with the tide, the spuds providing sufficient anchorage. In the normal operating position the hull was raised 6in above the free floatation level. This imposed a load of 42 tons on each spud. In heavy weather the spuds were supposed to lift the pontoon at least 12in. But they were not designed to lift or hold the pontoon completely out of the water.
>
> The pontoon itself, like a small ship, was 200ft long, 60ft wide and had a moulded depth of 10ft at the sides. The total weight, including the spuds, was around 1,100 tons. Internally, it was divided into watertight compartments and there was room to accommodate the operating crew of one officer, six NCOs and fifteen men. It was equipped with kitchen, sanitation and heating appliances.

There were also variants on the basic model, as Lt. Col. Ronnie Cowan, Commander of 969 & 970 Companies who planted floating piers and roadways, relates:

There was also a special pierhead to handle Tank Landing Ships (LSTs). In the ordinary way the large Landing Ship Tanks were run on the beaches as high as the tide would allow and, on flat beaches, the vehicles emerging from the bow doors had to drive through a water gap to reach dry land. LSTs had a draught at the bow end of 4 ft. 6 ins. and 11 ft. 6 ins. at the stern when fully loaded. They had a dead weight of 2500 tons when fully loaded.

The LST pierhead was formed by setting two spud pierheads at right angles to each other, but connected by a telescopic bridge span.

One pierhead was 'set' normally to the pontoon bridge, the other at a right angle to it.

Attached to the first pierhead were two wedge shaped buffer pontoons which acted as false beaches and on to which the LSTs ran their bows. The surface of these steel pontoons was 'dished' so that the ship bows were guided to the centre line of the pontoon.

Mr George Youngs, Chief Designer at Lobnitz, now aged 90, said that one of the unexpected problems encountered by the soldiers monitoring the tidal changes while seated in front of the dials in the spud pontoon cabin, was their tendency to fall asleep. The warmth of the cabin and the monotony of the task made it difficult to stay awake. A series of alarm bells were installed in the cabin and even hand signals similar to those found by railway lines were attached to the pontoon legs, but to no avail. Eventually a rota was implemented with a change of duty every hour.

If the spud pontoon was notable for its size, the floating roadway was no less so for sheer ingenuity and for standing on its head the conventional approach to bridge design. In outline terms the floating roadway is easily described. It comprised a series of linked spans, 80 feet long with a 10-foot-wide roadway. The spans were founded on floating pontoons or Beetles and the seaward end of the roadway was linked to the Whale pier. Linked spans were required to form a continuous roadway up to one mile long. The difficulty of course, was that the whole construction would have to be built on the ever-moving sea. Each span weighed 28 tons. As Allan Beckett succinctly put it:

> The usual conception of a bridge structure is one in which stiffness and
> rigidity are very desirable features, whilst the bridge supports are
> expected to stay put within an inch or two. It is not unusual for a bridge
> designer to view his supports and foundations with some pessimism and
> this case was no exception. Consideration was given to the design of a
> bridge span which would be safe under excessive movement of its
> foundations. In the worst case (that of a pontoon bridge), it is assumed
> that the bridge spans must allow for movement in the supports
> corresponding to the behaviour of small boats in a very rough sea.

It was Lt.Col. William Everall, who was in charge of the overall design of the spans of the bridge. He was a railway engineer who had acquired an almost legendary reputation in north-west India. After being appointed Chief Bridging Instructor, No. 2 Railway Training Centre, Derby in September, 1939, he was asked to design a flexible gangway to enable locomotives to be loaded and unloaded from a Channel ferry steamer. Using spherical bearings, his assistant Allan Beckett made it possible for a span to twist through an angle of six degrees, conforming to the motion of the vessel.

For Mulberry, Beckett used spherical bearings to enable the pontoon-mounted spans to twist in rough seas. They allowed a free angular movement of one span relative to another of 24 degrees, and a torsional displacement of 40 degrees along the length of each span. The spans were also designed to be immensely strong so that in extreme conditions, when phasing of the wave coincided with the distance between pontoons, the pontoons in the wave troughs could be lifted clear of the water while the pontoons on the wave crests would be submerged.

A further innovation was the telescopic span, which allowed for an increase or reduction in span length about its centre. This ingenious development solved several problems at a stroke — it enabled the bridge to adjust to variation in the height of the tides, and it meant that any lateral displacement of the roadway in rough seas, which would make the bridge longer, could be accommodated. The telescopic span was also used to simplify the linking of adjacent pierheads. Its telescopic nature meant that the pierheads did not have to be placed too accurately, as any misalignment could be taken up by the sliding span.

It is interesting to note that at a later date, Allan Beckett, when writing about Everall's work, was a welding enthusiast.

> The very fine limits of accuracy that are obtainable by welded fabrication are emphasized in this design [of the telescopic span] which uses black finish throughout and no machining other than for normal plate-edge preparation.

At the time that Mulberry was built, welding was a new technology and was regarded with scepticism by engineers; they still preferred riveting as a means of joining metal. With steel in short supply, the switch to welding saved considerable amounts of this precious metal.

It was fortunate that the Whale (pierheads) proved stable without anchors; but anchors were found to be necessary for other parts of the harbour, and Allan Beckett faced the problem of anchoring the floating roadways.

> At this stage my link with the War Office moved to Lt. Col Steer-Webster RE who, like Everall, had a special gift for getting things done. He also had the ear of Winston Churchill. Steer-Webster insisted that every last detail of equipment, tools and procedure for assembly of floating bridges

and pier head pontoons on an enemy shore should be properly worked out and that the equipment be simple, easy and quick to use even in bad weather.

In order to anchor the floating bridge so that it would provide a secure roadway, little lateral movement under sea conditions would be tolerated, and a stretched cable system was adopted to give the necessary measure of control. This called for a light anchor that was able to resist a 30 ton pull.

No such anchor existed so I was given a research contract with Messrs Braithwaite under which they would produce six anchors to my design, each weighing about 4cwt, and test them by hauling with a winch over simulated seabed conditions. To achieve the required performance it was necessary for the anchor to bury itself in the seabed.

As a preliminary, I made several tin plate models and experimented by dragging them through mud at the beach near Erith Yacht Club where I kept my yacht.

The first four prototypes made by Braithwaite failed to bury themselves sufficiently to pick up any substantial load. However, we took the most promising of the anchors, modified the buoyant stock, and reshaped the point of entry, and this produced the desired effect. An anchorage resisting a 30 ton pull could be found in a wide range of seabed materials.

Bruce White took great interest in the solution to the anchor problem and arranged for a sea test for HMS *Barham*, a boom defence vessel stationed in Scotland. I was sent to witness the test.

The skipper of this vessel made no secret of his scepticism of my claim for the holding power of the anchor — perhaps because as it lay on the afterdeck it looked small and something of a toy. The scale of the load clock provided did not exceed 30 ton and the skipper asked me what size of wire should be attached, mentioning that the thimble on the anchor was made to suit a steel wire rope of 4¼" circumference. I suggested that he choose a size that he considered appropriate. With a great show of indifference he attached a 3½" circumference steel wire rope as an anchor cable.

The vessel was steamed full ahead, the anchor was thrown over the stern and the cable was veered to an extent of 12 times the water depth, then secured through the load clock to a stout bollard. The ship was brought up all standing and the anchor cable sang like a harp string. The crew, who knew what damage a broken cable can do, vanished from the afterdeck in a flash.

On examination the load clock needle was bent. The skipper muttered something like 'It must have caught on a rock'.

We weighed the anchor quite easily and made a second test with the same result: I felt sure that the skipper had by then changed his opinion of the anchor. It was given the name 'Kite' because of its burying capability under a balance of forces similar to those that cause the uplift of a kite, but of course in reverse.

I have been asked as to whether the kite anchor did in fact bury itself in the rocky outcrops of the beach at Arromanches. Where these rocks were exposed at low tide we took no chances, and with a bulldozer scraped a hole into which the anchor was pushed. However, for the most part the anchors were totally or partially buried by the pull of the cable. When Mulberry was ultimately dismantled very few anchors were recovered because the cables broke in the attempt to disengage them from the sea bed.

The use of the new type of anchor required new techniques in handling, as Prof. Sir Alan Harris explains:

Careful thought was given to the placing of these anchors and the setting of their moorings; special craft were designed. The key craft was the 'mooring shuttle', a low-freeboard twin-hulled craft with a cable drum amidships between the hulls and an anchor fore and aft. The shuttles were carried over on the decks of the Whale tows, and were launched by rolling down a ramp on the cable drum which projected below the hull. Once afloat, they were picked up by a specially designed motor-boat, flat-bottomed, small draught and freeboard, again made of plywood, known as a Slug (Surf Landing Under Girder), developed in collaboration with Camper & Nicholson.

Having picked up the shuttle, the Slug tows it to the upstream anchor position, where one anchor with the cable is dropped by opening a flap; the Slug then tows the shuttle, paying out the cable as it goes, under the bridge and through a bight of rope slung below the bridge to where the downstream anchor is dropped, again by opening a flap. The bight of the rope is then hauled up and the cable comes up with it and is fixed by stoppers on the pontoon deck. A Yale 'pull-lift' [sic] winch grips the cable by a loose stopper, tensions it, and the slack is taken up by the stopper on deck. No winches are thus needed on the pontoons; a very neat operation.

Every aspect of Mulberry development called for innovation against an appallingly tight deadline. New ideas had to be tested, developed and manufactured while other components were in full production: this was especially true of the Tn5 pierhead. The pontoons on which the bridge sections floated were a wholly new model, as Allan Beckett explains in the following extract:

In describing the design of the pontoons some of the requirements must be emphasised. It was essential that they should be absolutely seaworthy and as nearly unsinkable as possible, also cheap to produce and in large numbers. They had to support, at a high level, moving 'dead' loads and moving 'live' loads [tanks etc.] considerably in excess of their own weight. In addition they had to impart the minimum of shock load to the bridge spans in rough sea conditions and to avoid overtwisting them. Finally it was required that they should be towed sideways without undue resistance and carry their loads when grounding in a surf on a beach which might be sand or rock.

A naval architect might be excused if he stated that the problem would not yield to a practical solution. The engineer, of course, simply has to produce his design by a given date.

The testing and development of the Mulberry harbour in Garlieston was a serious matter of national importance. There was, however, a lighter side, as Fraser Evans, a local farmer, relates:

> Living on and farming the lands of Penkiln, Garlieston, we look down on the harbour of Garlieston, looking for all the world as though it were the stage of a giant amphitheatre. Therefore, we can't help but see all that is going on in the harbour. Normally the activities were the coming in and out of the local fishing boats and the occasional coastal steamers with various cargoes for the feed mill situated at the harbour.
>
> But in 1943 all this changed, and fussy little tugs started pulling into the harbour, from places unknown, a whole variety of structures, some floating on their own, and others in barges which looked as though they would be more at home in inland waterways. But they were all dwarfed by a magnificent 60 ton floating crane which was towed in and tied up at the end of the pier. From then on there was constant activity in the harbour area, and in command of the crane was a very pleasant sergeant with whom I became friendly. This was for three reasons: firstly he was a very nice fellow, secondly he made very good strong, sweet tea, and thirdly at 9 p.m. every night, he lifted the phone and got an up-to-date weather forecast, a point that went down very well on the farm.
>
> It is known now what the purpose of the great activity was, but at that time it was a complete mystery. Some incidents were quite hilarious. I remember the day a Landing Craft Tank (LCT) came steaming into the beach at Garlieston, dropped its stern anchors, let down the loading ramp and with much huffing and puffing, rolled out what I called the 'magic carpet', or Swiss Rolls, which consisted of wooden railway sleeper-like slats, covered with canvas and held together by a series of wire hawsers. When they finally got it unrolled to the water's edge, they then dug in shore anchors. The LCT then pulled back and made all taut. Down the ramps of the LCT came a ten-ton army lorry, camouflaged and complete with canvas cover. For a magic moment it seemed to run over the top of the water, and

one's mind went back to the event in the Sea of Galilee, but the further it got from the LCT, the lower in the water it sank, and then the anchors must have dragged, because with hilarious swiftness the water was up to and passing the driver's door. He, with the dexterity of a Madagascan monkey, was out, up and sitting on top of the canvas cover, in a trice. The soldiers, whether the officers were looking at them or not, were falling about with laughter. Of course, when the tide went out, all was retrieved.

Then there was the day of a near full gale blowing in from the south by south-west. A succession of great white, bearded seas were marching with majestic power and determination almost straight into Garlieston Bay. Imagine my surprise and amazement when I perceived the two sea-going tugs with great difficulty pulling a line of Beetles out to sea, and at the back like a puppy dog was the *Ajay*, a small tug, acting as a rudder at the rear. On the bridges as ever, was the ten-ton lorry, complete with driver, who was manfully trying to drive the lorry up and down the alarmingly rising and falling and corkscrewing section of bridges. All this in itself could have been said to be awe-inspiring, but added to that was the fact that when in the trough of the waves, bridges, pontoons and lorry disappeared from sight.

A thought struck me, 'How in the name of heaven are they ever going to get this lot turned in that sea and brought back into harbour?'

But that was the least of the problems, because one of the tow ropes from a tug to the bridges, broke, and the inboard end must have wrapped round the propeller, because the tug started to drift helplessly onto Eggerness Point. The other tug let go its tow rope and headed inland and dragged the first tug off the rocks. This left the tiny *Ajay* with smoke belching out of her diesel engine in such profusion that one could have been forgiven for thinking she was coal-fired, trying to keep afloat the bridges plus army lorry and driver, who was sitting there waiting for the inevitable, having abandoned trying to drive up and down. The *Ajay* had at last to let go and we all watched the string of bridges and the army lorry, plus driver, land on the rocks of Eggerness shore. The lorry, driver, some Beetles and all the steel work were salvaged, but to this day there still remain one or two of the Beetles lying there.

The difficulties posed by the weather are never far away in the history of Mulberry development. In the end, it was the weather that proved to be the real test of the three ideas under trial. Allan Beckett takes up the story.

> Two other possible solutions to the problem of 'piers for flat beaches' were put under trial at Cairn Head, namely the 'Hamilton Swiss Roll' and 'Hughes Caisson Scheme'. A fourth idea which was an adapted Bailey Bridge was also being tested at Westward Ho.

I made many trips to Cairn Head but the most memorable was the one I made after a few days of stormy weather when Brigadier Bruce White instructed me to go and witness the effect of storm damage on the prototypes. I spent the whole of the overnight journey wondering and worrying about what had gone wrong and quite expected to see my floating bridge a mass of broken twisted metal. Lt. Col. Sainsbury met me at Carlisle and when I asked him what had been happening his reply was 'You had better see for yourself'.

As we approached the coast the noise of the sea and wind was deafening and the floating bridge was writhing and twisting in a sea that had already wrecked a fishing boat. The waves were breaking over the bridge and it needed good sea legs to walk along it BUT it was intact and fully workable. The Hamilton Swiss Roll had washed away and the Hughes Caisson Scheme had failed under the movement of its piers. After several days of rough weather it was not difficult for the Chiefs of Staff to make a choice.

They were given a demonstration of tanks and road vehicles going over the floating bridges on to a spud pontoon.

By early July 1943 the requirements for Overlord had been enumerated and the Chiefs of Staff had no alternative but to approve the Tn5 scheme. They ordered four miles of pier and six pierheads, which were to be ready by 1st February, 1944.

In August 1943 the decision was made to build a total of 22 pierheads. They were to be built at three sites in Scotland and Wales. The contract for all the work was placed by the Ministry of Supply with Alexander Findlay & Co., Ltd., Bridgebuilders, Motherwell. Thirteen pierheads and sixteen intermediate pontoons were to be built at Findlay's revamped yard in Leith; three pierheads were built by Port Construction and Repair Companies on a slipway to the north of No 2 Military Port at Cairnryan; and five pierheads and four buffer pontoons were built at Conway's Morfa estate.

It was essential that the pierheads were built in a shipyard or yards as they had to be launched. This too required a novel approach as at both Scottish yards it was necessary to adopt broadside launching.In 1943, this type of launching was common in the USA, but no one had tried it in the UK with anything as large as a Mulberry pierhead.

Welding, rather than rivets, was to be used whenever possible to save steel. Much of this work was done by men from trades such as hairdressing and tailoring who had no previous knowledge of welding. At Cairnryan the sappers were unable to weld and instruction took place whenever men were free from other duties.

But a shock was in store. After allowing 8–10 weeks for fitting-out the yards, the building time for each pierhead would need to be slashed from the four months required for the prototype to just four weeks; Pearson Lobnitz was adamant that it could not be done.

But it was P W Robson, Findlay's Chairman, who moved the design from that of a prototype to a production model. He redisigned all the welded elements of the pierhead, making it possible for novice welders to work on them. This freed-up the expert welders for more difficult tasks. He also devised prefabricated units, some weighing seven tons, for especially difficult parts. In this way, work which occupied two weeks on the prototype took only a few hours.

In addition to the manpower require to build the pierheads, resources were also required to man them in action. When Lt. Col. Cowan received his initial instructions concerning his involvement with Mulberry, he was delighted to learn that

> . . . orders had already been passed to every RE Unit in the United
> Kingdom to send, immediately, their finest, bravest and most highly
> skilled soldiers to join this crack invasion force, because 'Mulberry Must
> Not Fail'.

His delight was, however, short-lived as

> Alas, what really happened was that every unit in the UK seized this
> golden opportunity to 'unload' on to us their most formidable and
> desperate criminals. Tough looking men arrived clutching Crime Sheets
> covering every known offence: insolence, theft, wife beating, assault and
> battery, robbery with violence, larceny and desertion, etc. etc. As they
> paraded we eyed each other — it was obvious that they didn't think
> much of us, while we could tell that Mulberry and the invasion were not
> going to be a success.
>   In the spring of 1944, in March, April and May, Captain Tarling and
> his experienced NCOs gradually began to turn the very mixed company
> of men into soldiers. This was a most difficult task; the 'rejects' sent to us
> by other Engineer Units managed to pillage and loot the surrounding
> villages. They set fire to Glasserton House [near Garlieston], they
> wrecked a great deal of valuable equipment at Ryde: George Tarling had
> some 22 Court-martials in process or pending at the end of May.
>   A visiting Colonel, watching an unhappy squad being trained in the
> use of the Bren gun on the lawn at Glasserton House, remarked 'These
> men will never make soldiers; what a bunch of bloody goons.' The name
> stuck, but in the event the 'Goons' were magnificent.
>   We did our best but training was badly restricted because the
> equipment, the piers and the pierheads, were still being built and
> delivered. Ted Witcomb took over the pierheads at Southampton Docks
> where, we found, he became Chairman of a daily conference of Captains
> RN, Senior US Army Officers etc. Ted seemed quite at home and able,

with great tact and charm, to instruct these Officers so that the pierheads were commissioned and passed speedily over to the Americans and British crews.

We continually begged Colonel Mais for a full scale exercise — which he was most anxious to arrange.

In May he told us that a rehearsal had been arranged, the date fixed, the 6th of June.

Next we heard — and the Colonel was oddly coy and evasive — that this exercise had been postponed — but that we must not worry, we would be given a chance to put the equipment together under the most rigorous conditions 'very soon'.

Later on Raymond Mais told us how, enraged at this postponement, he had stormed into 30 Corps Headquarters and demanded that his men **must** be allowed to practice with the equipment before D-day. He was taken aside by a Colonel of Intelligence who told him that there were very, very good reasons why the exercise could not be held. Mais still refused to accept this and continued to argue; the Intelligence Officer, with a hopeless look on his face, asked 'cannot even you think of one day on which you will be otherwise engaged'.

At last the penny dropped and Colonel Mais realised that the date for the invasion had been fixed — for 6th June, 1944.

There were other lighter moments too. Barry Stewart of Stranraer recalls a story told by his father John, a private in the Royal Engineers, who had good cause to remember his posting to Cairnryan in early 1944:

Having been separated by war from this wife and two children living in Stranraer, he received a posting from overseas to Cairnryan in order to assist in the construction of Mulberry. He was informed that the work at Cairnryan was top secret and was warned that under no circumstances was he or any other soldier stationed there to leave the port.

Many months of separation from his wife and family and the lure of Stranraer were too much for the soldier and, acting without authority, he managed to hitch a lift to Stranraer with the intention of paying a visit to his home.

Met by a friend while out shopping in Stranraer on the same day, John's wife was told that her husband must be on leave as he had been in town.

'That's impossible,' the wife said, 'my husband is still abroad — in Egypt I think.'

Before John could make contact with his wife, however, he was apprehended by the Military Police and duly escorted to Cairnryan to await a court martial for being absent without leave.

The story has a happy ending, however. The Commanding Officer being a family man himself, no doubt, severely reprimanded the hapless sapper for his insubordination but promptly dropped the charges.

And Anne Bartlet of West Linton is happy to remember her time at Cairnryan as she met her husband there:

> I was in the Church of Scotland Hut at Cairnryan for three years. We served Thames lightermen, Welsh quarrymen and saw the Spuds and Whales being made. Colonel Stork and Major MacFadzean and Major Cramb are the names I remember there. We were so busy there was not much time for speculation of what it was all about. It was very hard work but we had lots of fun. The local ladies helped us in the evenings and each night had a different 'flavour'. There wasn't much time for individuals, but we wrote letters and such for the sappers. I remember 'Spud' who adopted us and once a week he and a group scrubbed the floor for us. He had learned this in Wormwood Scrubs and was proud of the fact he had volunteered. A Black Maria met him when on leave and he didn't have to struggle with transport home. Some of the sappers were so home sick I think the hut helped to alleviate the trauma for some, especially if their wives were bombed out in London or Hull.

The spud legs of the Cairnryan pierheads were added at Faslane, on the west coast of Scotland, some 131 miles from Cairnryan[4]. After fitting, the operation of the legs was tested. Thomas Coughtrie, an electrical engineer who was employed by the Chief Inspector of Electrical & Mechanical Equipment for Forces, recalls one such test:

> The first pierhead test at Faslane was rewarding because the trip on the loch [Gare Loch] was almost a pleasant excursion to some — there were also those of rank who were buoyed up by a good lunch and aperitifs. I was on tenterhooks because I had tested and certified nearly all the machinery and control gear. With the amount of welding going on, cables were always at risk of being burned through or scorched.
>
> Not many yards off, alongside a rocky shore, the pierhead lay quietly. There was no wind and the ubiquitous midge was a pest. The two nearest spud legs, each 90 feet long, were lowered slowly into the loch until they touched the bottom. When they were fully on the bottom the spuds were only half down, the water being about 30–40 feet deep. Next the two spuds furthest from the shore were winched down . . . and down . . . until they reached the limit of their downward travel. But they hadn't reached the bottom! Hastily, a measuring tape was tied to a bolt and lowered as a

---

[4] The pierheads manufactured at Leith and Morfa had their spud legs fitted at Southampton

sounding line . . . without touching bottom. The bold mariners aboard
had not availed themselves of a chart, so speculation arose as to the
possiblity of the pierhead being positioned over a cavity on the loch bed.
So the spuds were lifted and we moved on 100 yards. With the pierhead
still about the same distance from the shore, the exercise was repeated
with the same result. The sides of the loch shelved more steeply than the
roof of a house. This sobering fact alerted all non swimmers aboard and a
lively interest arose in the two liferafts suspended at either end of the
vessel; there were no lifebelts or Mae Wests. The tests were now restarted
with the pierhead much nearer the shore. To test the flotation gear I tilted
the vessel — in a few moments the pierhead lost all its passengers who
stepped nimbly ashore to attend to more pressing business.

In the winter of 1943, Thomas Coughtrie was following a punishing itinerary,
travelling hundreds of miles a week by road and rail, often to the detriment of his
own health: he collapsed during a transformer trial in Edinburgh. At the time of his
collapse he weighed 10 stone — he was 6 feet 1 inch tall. When asked if he was fit
enough to go on, he replied only that when his job was done could he be allowed to
transfer to a Midlands department so that he could recover his health at home.

Thomas Coughtrie was involved in the first launch at Leith:

I was on board when the first production pierhead slid down the ways on
26th January, 1944. It was a time of feverish activity. Each pierhead was
constructed lying parallel to the shore; the launching was a spectacle
indeed: some 1000 tons of pierhead racing towards the water at high tide.
It struck the sea with such force that everyone on board was knocked off
their feet, and those who had not gone up to the bridges were swamped.

I was nonchalantly gripping a handrail with one hand, and this proved
to be my undoing. I was laid flat on my face with a wrist sorely twisted. But
there was work to be done. I pulled myself together and slid down the guard
rails to the deck and then helter-skeltered down the companionway to the
generator area where I started the diesels. This was done to provide power
for the capstans and winches so that the pierhead could be warped to the
shore, and also to provide power for the pumps as it was expected that hull
plates could be staved in and sprung owing to the shock of hitting the water.
There was a tremendous amount of activity, everybody knew just what to
do and quite a few shed blood and skinned knees and knuckles in their
valiant efforts to secure their precious vessel.

When American troops were allocated pierheads, they adapted them further, as
Thomas Coughtrie recalls:

In general the Americans were splendid. They seemed to have no fear of
retribution if things went wrong — no fear of any consequences. This
became evident when they took over their first pierhead.

At once, acetylene cutting gear was borrowed and they set about burning away all the cross-struts and stays inside the crew accommodation and sleeping areas, where the bunks were placed — as it was, it would have been impossible to sit up in bed owing to the proximity of criss-crossed angle beams. With all the structural members removed, they took immediate advantage of the dollar exchange rate in a local town. One of their numerous vehicles was requisitioned for a shopping spree and the 'tween-deck' of their pierhead was transformed; it was repainted and in went carpets, chairs, sofas, tables and pictures — even cutlery and china were on the list. It was a local bonanza with everything paid for in cash.

The construction of the spud pontoons underlines Scottish industry's considerable contribution to the war effort. More than 100 Scottish firms sent 30,000 tons of steelwork and machinery to Normandy; 83 per cent of the pierheads were supplied from Scotland.

The Lobnitz dredger *Lucayan* in Valparaiso

Garlieston Bay and the Galloway Hills

Major Carline; Maj. Steer-Webster, QMG Thomas Riddell-Webster, Brig. Bruce White arriving at Garlieston Harbour, 13th March 1943

Maj. Carline, QMG Thomas Riddell-Webster, Brig. Bruce White, Maj. Steer-Webster examining plans at Garlieston, 13th March 1943

H 28115 © Imperial War Museum, London

Royal Engineer diver preparing to make a sea bed reconnaisance on a floating pier, 13th March 1943

Concrete pontoon used for the floating pier section (Beetle), Garlieston Harbour, 13th March 1943

River tugs towing spud pontoon from Gareloch to the boom on the Clyde, April 1943

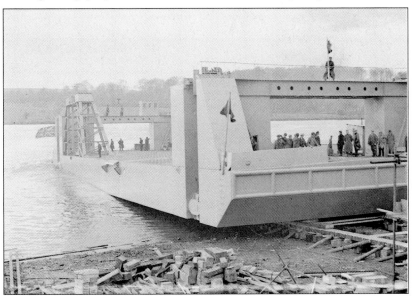

Launching prototype Spud Pontoon 'Winnie' at Old Kilpatrick, Clydeside, 7th April 1943

'Winnie' on tow, after launching at Old Kilpatrick

Spud pontoons at Alex Findlay's yard, Leith

©Lobnitz

Spud pontoon off Leith, April 1943

H 29419 © Imperial War Museum, London

Left to right: Brig. Bruce White, Mr Pearson Lobnitz, Capt. H C McIntyre and
Lt. Col. J Sainsbury on deck of spud pontoon, Cairnryan, April 1943

General view of complete structure of spud pontoon and floating pier at high water, May 1943

Floating Pierhead under stress during gale at Cairn Head, May 1943

H 29797 © Imperial War Museum, London

Floating pierhead under stress during gale at Cairn Head, showing twisting effect, May 1943

H30527 © Imperial War Museum, London

Lifting Swiss Roll section from barge in Garlieston Harbour, May 1943

Unrolling Swiss Roll by towing, Garlieston Harbour, 28th May 1943

Hippo No. 1 arriving at Rigg Bay anchorage, Garlieston, 28th May 1943

High officers of the Allied Armies and Navies arriving at Cairn Head for demonstration of the D Tn Scheme – The Engineer-in-Chief Maj. General C J S King (later Sir Charles) in foreground and Brig. Bruce White – Cairn Head, 29th June 1943

H 30922 © Imperial War Museum, London

Line of vehicles coming ashore from pierhead at Cairn Head, 29th June 1943

H 30930 © Imperial War Museum, London

Swiss Rolls ready for towing at Garlieston, 29th June 1943

Vehicles on Swiss Roll at Cairn Head, 2nd July 1943

Right to left: Maj. Carline, Brig. Bruce White, Mr Ronald Hamilton (inventor of Swiss Roll) and his son at Cairn Head, 2nd July 1943

Hauling Swiss Roll ashore by tractor, Cairn Head, 2nd July 1943

Swiss Roll mat (Mk11) showing bulge, Garlieston, 9th July 1943

Vehicles on Swiss Roll at Cairn Head, 2nd July 1943

Truck on Swiss Roll showing 22" water on mat after 26 minutes, 5th August, 1943

Aerial view of spud pontoon at Cairn Head, August 1943

Two pierheads, Leith

Work on spud pontoons at Alex Findlay's yard, Leith

Brig. Bruce White (right) explains details of floating pier attachment to Gen. Charles King (centre) and General Donald McMullen (left), 18th June, 1943

H 30932 © Imperial War Museum, London

Tank at speed on the floating pier at Cairn Head, 18th June 1943

General view of Hippos, 5th August 1943

H 30929 © Imperial War Museum, London

H 31626 © Imperial War Museum, London

Transport arriving at spud pontoon, Cairn Head, 5th August 1943

US Army officers watching demonstration of Swiss Roll at Cairn Head, 23rd August 1943

Beetle pontoon being towed from Garlieston to Cairn Head, October 1943

Heading towards the rocks in Garlieston Bay to remove bridge spans from rocks, 17th January 1944

Removing the first span of bridging from rocks, 17th January 1944

Whale pier and slipway, Cairnryan, 8th February 1944

Foundations of the new Whale to be built at Cairnryan, 8th February 1944

Erection tank being towed out of Garlieston by tug *Ajay*, 17th February 1944

H 35925 © Imperial War Museum, London

Construction of Whale at Cairnryan, 17th February 1944

H 35937 © Imperial War Museum, London

Caisson being towed from Findlay's Yard after completion

© North Lanarkshire Council Leisure Services

Five-span bridge ready to be towed over measured mile in Garlieston harbour, 11th March 1944

Tug *Ebro* towing five-span bridge over measured mile, 11th March 1944

Landing of shore ramp showing gear used in landing with spans on a beach shore, behind Garlieston harbour, 15th March 1944

Lobnitz pier at Mulberry A off Omaha beach, Normandy, June 1944

LST 543, the first landing ship to unload at Mulberry A, June 1944

LSTs unloading at Omaha beach before Mulberry A was established. Barrage balloons hover over assemblage of shipping as the Allies pour in supplies for the armies ashore.

US National Archives Record Administration

A section of the Gooseberry breakwater created from a line of sunken ships, adjacent to Mulberry A. The major role of this line was to offer a mooring place for small craft, June 1944

US National Archives Record Administration

The damage caused by the channel storm that hit directly after the completion of the Mulberry. Boats and ships of all sizes were strewn about in a jumbled mass of wreckage, June 1944

The floating repair shop which the US Navy Seabees moored in Mulberry A. It was invaluable for repairing what could be salvaged after the storm, June 1943

All hands pitch in to keep the flow of supplies going at a pierhead in Mulberry A, June 1944

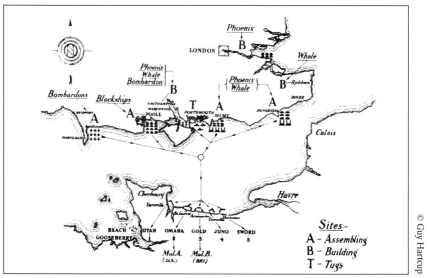

Map of Mulberry assembly and dispersal

© Guy Hartcup

Aerial view of Mulberry B at Arromanches, June 1944

© Imperial War Museum, London

Barbara Scott-Jupp (née Lane) of the Queen Alexandra's Imperial Military Nursing Service went over to Normandy with a mobile regimental first aid post

Cartoon of Lt. Col. R J P Cowan by Byrne

Cartoon of a 'Goon' by Lt. Col. R J P Cowan

Top left: Mr Pearson Lobnitz
Top right: Maj. Gen. Sir Harold Wernher
Bottom left: Major Alan Harris
Bottom right: Mr George Youngs

SHELTERED WATER

The first reaction of everyone to the [Phoenix] units was: 'Will it float or will it sink?' My boss said simply: 'If it sinks you'll probably be drafted in the army pretty quick.'
— Bob Nivison formerly of Arthur Monk & Co., Site Engineer Phoenix construction site, Barking Creek

Although, as Beckett had reported, the Tn5 solution withstood a considerable battering in the Solway, it was widely accepted that sheltered water was a prerequisite for the success of Mulberry; ships and landing craft could not berth at an unsheltered harbour in bad weather, however robust it might be.

It is thought that John Hughes-Hallett, then a Commodore in the Royal Navy and later a Vice Admiral, first proposed the necessity for an area of sheltered water in order to supply the troops and maintain the impetus of the invasion after the initial landing. Hughes-Hallett had almost certainly thought long and hard about the problem of invading the Continent as he had been the naval commander at the ill-fated Dieppe raid and, by 1943, was the naval Chief of Staff to the planners of Operation Overlord. But Hughes-Hallett was reported as saying that 'an engineer called Guy Maunsell' had shown him plans for an artificial breakwater as early as 1940.

The top brass became convinced of the need for sheltered water at the time of the Quebec conference in August 1943. Guy Hartcup writes:

> A selection of senior officers was assembled in one of the ship's [Queen Mary] luxurious bathrooms where a demonstration was given by Professor J D Bernal, the eminent physicist and one of Mountbatten's scientific advisers. Standing on a lavatory seat, Admiral Sir Dudley Pound, First Sea Lord, invited his colleagues to imagine the shallow end of the bath as a beachhead. Bernal now floated, with the assistance of Lt-Cdr D A Grant, a fleet of 20 ships made of newspaper.
>   Grant was then requested to make waves with the aid of a backbrush. The fleet sank. A Mae West lifebelt was then inflated and floated in the bath so as to represent a harbour. The fleet of paper boats was then placed inside it. Once more Grant applied his brush vigorously to create waves, but this time they failed to sink the fleet. By such simple means were the senior officers convinced of the importance of sheltered water.

Naval ideas for a sheltered harbour were, naturally, based on a naval solution: that is, the use of scuttled blockships. Numerous other approaches to wave suppression were investigated by DMWD. Possible solutions included large inflatable rubber bags evolved from lilos; enormous concrete 'caissons'; and a submerged pipe through which compressed air was blown to form a screen of bubbles — the Bubble Breakwater. Major-General Wernher recalls one proposal submitted to him:

> Whilst at COSSAC, owing to the fact that I had been at Combined
> Operations, I continued to be asked to investigate fantastic schemes. On
> one occasion a prominent United States General, in the Corps of
> Engineers, sent me this proposal. He suggested that, as there were a great
> many surplus aeroplane engines, these should be mounted on barges and
> anchored some way from the shore. The engines should then be started
> up and would run continuously when there was a gale blowing for, by
> this means, he imagined that the wind would be deflected from the
> *Mulberry* harbours. In the first place, there was no great surplus of
> aeroplane engines and, secondly, the number of engines required for the
> job under his scheme would absorb more petrol than the whole
> Expeditionary Force was estimated to use. Scientifically the proposal was
> unsound, because there is no known way of deflecting a gale, which
> naturally commences many miles from the shore. It was sometimes
> difficult to give a polite answer to this type of proposition.

The final solution was to be an artificial breakwater comprising three elements (the Navy was not convinced that concrete caissons would be any good). First, an inner line of blockships made up from 59 defunct ships that were to be sunk using explosives — this line was codenamed Gooseberry. The second line was to be formed by 200 huge concrete caissons. When in place this Phoenix element of the breakwater would stretch for 20,000 feet (almost four miles) and for half its length it would need to be 60 feet high. The third, outermost line of the breakwater would be formed from floating steel sections, cruciform in cross section, called Bombardons. The navy were to be responsible for Gooseberies and Bombardons, the Army for Phoenix. Vice Admiral Hickling takes up the the story of the breakwater's make-up.

> The first form of breakwater and probably the simplest was the blockship
> which, as I have already said, was used for the Gooseberries. They
> consisted of such old merchant ships as we could get hold of and they had
> the great advantage that, being mobile, they did not require any tugs (for
> in this venture tugs were worth their weight in gold). They could get
> themselves from 'A' to 'B' and manoeuvre themselves roughly into
> position and so provide essential protection from D-day onwards They
> were ballasted to draw about 19 ft. of water, and filled with explosive
> charges of ten pounds of *amatol* on each side of each hold, which were
> connected up electrically to a central firing key. When they were in the
> right place to be 'planted' as we called it, the charges were fired and blew
> a hole 3 ft. below the water line, and down the ships went. We also had
> alternative methods of firing by time fuse. HMS *Vernon* took every sort
> of precaution to avoid any hitch but one thing was overlooked — the rats

which ate the insulation of the electric wires. Fortunately we spotted this in time and all was well.

If ever you have to plant blockships remember this, the ships should be locked well in, *ie*, they should overlap, there should be no gaps otherwise scour will take place, the ends of the ships will become unsupported and, as happened in the American harbour, they will break their backs.

The depth of the average tramp, such as we got, is of the order of 40 ft. from keel to upper deck. This meant that, with a rise of tide of 23 ft., the depth in which the blockships could be sunk to make effective breakwaters was about 15 ft. at low water. A breakwater which is submerged at high water is not much use.

It was a comparatively simple business to fit out these blockships but to obtain the sixty old ships we needed was not so easy. At this time — December, 1943, the heavy sinkings of Allied shipping by the U-boat packs in the Atlantic were still fresh in people's minds, and when Admiral Tennant and I went to the Admiralty and said we wanted all those ships just to sink off the coast of Normandy to make the five Gooseberries we were very nearly thrown out. As we came away somewhat chastened I said to Tennant: 'Bill, we came here to get a Gooseberry and all we seem to have got is a raspberry'.

However, the request was considered by the Chiefs of Staff the following day and, although I was not present myself, I have a pretty shrewd idea that the argument must have gone something like this:

'Supposing for a moment we do get one of those infrequent summer gales and supposing the landing craft ferrying the stuff ashore to the beaches are driven ashore and cast up high and dry and the Army's life-line fails, are we — the Chiefs of Staff — prepared to face the country and say the Invasion has been defeated because we were unable to provide Admiral Ramsay with sixty old merchant ships?' So we got them. We also got a few old warships including the French battleship *Courbet*, the Dutch cruiser *Sumatra*, and the old target ship HMS *Centurion*.

The intention was to sink the blockships in shallow water — say 15 ft., and then to extend that breakwater East and West into deeper water by means of concrete caissons — the Phoenixes which I will describe shortly.

Although 'written-off', some of the blockships were raised after the war. The following extract is taken from the Glasgow Herald of July 1945:

A war-scarred ship, her sides streaked with rust over her wartime grey, was beached at Craigendoran, on the Firth of Clyde, last week. She is the *Parklaan*, of 5807 tons gross and is the first of the Mulberry block ships to raised from the English Channel. After removal of sand ballast she will be towed to Troon for breaking up.

She was beached between Craigendoran and Ardmore Point — an operation that mystified many who watched it. Lighters will remove the sand ballast and then she will be refloated and towed to the Troon shipbreaking yard of W H Arnott Young & Co., Ltd., Glasgow.

The second of the Navy's responsibilites was the innovative but not entirely succesful Bombardons. Vice Admiral Hickling again:

Outside each harbour, however, it was decided to put down a mile of floating breakwater called the 'Bombardon'. This was an entirely novel form of breakwater. The idea came to a fellow called Lochner, Lieutenant, RNVR, who was sitting one summer's afternoon in his garden alongside the swimming pool where a 'lilo', one of those rubber mattress affairs, was floating. Through his half-closed eyes he noticed the wavelets breaking up against the windward side of the lilo while on the lee side it was quite calm. That is how the Bombardon started. We actually got three mammoth rubber lilos, each 200 ft. long and about 15 ft. in diameter — the biggest rubber job Dunlops ever made. The concrete keel alone weighed 750 tons. They worked quite well while they lasted, but no practical sea-faring man wants to go into an operation of this sort with a lot of rubber hot water bottles hung round his neck!

The theory of these Bombardons was that when the sea hit the free-board they would start to oscillate, but they were so designed that the period of these oscillations would never come into phase with the period of the waves which it was intended to suppress. The wave for which they were designed and which we expected off the Normandy coast with a wind of force 6 to 7 say was 200 ft. crest to crest. The Bombardon had the advantage that it could be moored in comparatively deep water, say 60 ft., which would enable deeply-laden Liberty ships to anchor in its lee and discharge their cargoes under those difficult half and half conditions. A mile of Bombardons laid by D plus 8 at each Mulberry, (and so long as the conditions for which they were designed, ie, half a gale, were not exceeded they worked fairly well) gave a wave suppression of about 40 per cent. But on 19th June came the great storm, when they broke adrift from their moorings, and were wrecked on the beaches of Normandy. By some miracle they did not damage any ships as they drove ashore, nor did they damage any of the breakwaters, as some people have stated.

The Navy's Bombardon was an evolution of an earlier floating breakwater concept. The first models had flexible sides and it helped to prove to some extent the theories on which floating barrages were based. It appeared that the models could provide calm water as effectively as fixed breakwaters. The early design consisted of a rubberised canvas tube supported on a concrete keel. Three were launched in late

1943 but the design was abandoned because of the fragility of the canvas tubes. Thinking then turned to a rigid boom and the final configuration was more or less in the shape of a Maltese cross in section. Each unit was 200 feet long by 25 feet beam and 25 feet deep with a draught of 19 feet.

The Bombardons were made of steel plates and angles and they were bolted together. When launched, the bottom and side arms were filled with water to provide the mass required to combat wave action. In place the Bombardons were moored in pairs between buoys, and the layout adopted was two parallel lines, 800 feet apart. This arrangement was expected to reduce wave heights by some 70 per cent and wave energy by 90 per cent although, as we have seen in Vice Admiral Hickling's account it was more like 40 per cent.

As ever, even in matters of breakwater construction, the Army and the Navy were at odds. Allan Beckett recalls:

> Next they [the Navy] said: 'We can't get enough steel plate, you can use concrete.' I said we can't because of the rocks on the shore so they took the design to Mouchel[5]. It was agreed that we would use concrete for the pontoons (Beetles) but it was only 1¼ inches thick; it had to be thin to get the draught. They snapped the bridges on at Marchwood [Southampton Water] before they were cured and you could almost put your foot through the concrete.

Vice Admiral Hickling takes up the story again:

> As I have said, the Blockships and the Bombardons were a naval commitment. Now we come to the Army's part — the concrete caissons known as Phoenixes and the Whale Piers.
>
> The depth of the blockships confined them to comparatively shallow water. In order to provide breakwaters behind which Liberty ships drawing 26 or 27 ft. of water could berth, we had to go into the concrete business. The War Office designed the Phoenixes, which are nothing more nor less than concrete ships or hulks. They were not the best design but they were the best that could be made in the time. Always we were working against time: remember we had only seven months in which to do the job — a job which had never been done before — for our target date was 1st May, 1944. We had to go into production before the blueprints were off the drawing board, and we certainly had some teething troubles.
>
> There were half-a-dozen different sizes of Phoenixes depending on the depth of water in which they were to be planted, for they formed not only the outer breakwater but also the side arms. The A.1 — the biggest, was 200 ft. long, by 60 ft. high and 40 ft. beam. These blocks of flats had to

---

[5] L A Mouchel, Consulting Engineers

satisfy various conditions, the first of which was that they had to be towable, and that is why they were given swim (upswept) ends. They also had to be stable, that is, they had to remain on an even keel while they were being planted, for we did not want them capsizing. Most important of all, so far as the Navy was concerned — and it was the Navy who had to ' plant' them — was that they should sink quickly. You can imagine that 'planting' a 6,000 ton hulk with 40 ft. freeboard to catch the wind in any breeze and with a cross tide is no mean feat of seamanship, for they had to be placed with an accuracy not of feet but of inches. The first designs were going take the best part of an hour to sink, but eventually the War Office brought it down to about 15 minutes: that is to say, all except two which were being towed across the Channel after D-day, one of which was torpedoed, and one mined; they sank in 30 seconds.

The question was where to build these things, especially as we only had six months in which to do the job. We tried to get dry docks but the majority of these were already in use on shipping repair and also on a lot of jobs in connection with the assault itself. Remember, the assault was not a separate business from all this Mulberry operation, the Mulberry was a sort of poor relation and about as popular in assault circles. However, big holes were scratched out on the banks of tidal waters such as the Thames and Southampton Water, and the first 14 ft. of the Phoenixes were built there. When this was done the bank was broken down to let the water in and the sections were floated out and taken to adjacent wharves where they were completed. This process introduced all sorts of difficulties; for instance the Phoenix was designed as a complete structure, like a ship: building a bit of it and then floating it meant setting up all sorts of unfair stresses. It was only by a great deal of clever calculation, a certain amount of good fortune and prayer that it proved possible to fit the sections together without the whole structure breaking up. The first unit took about four months to build, but as things went on this was reduced to two months.

The construction of the components that comprised the Mulberry ports made considerable and severe demands on scarce wartime resources. In the following extract from Major-General Sir Harold Wernher's account, he provides a penetrating insight into the difficulties faced and their resolution.

The urgent task was to take up the labour, which I had asked for in August, for the construction of the *Phoenix*. Some twenty-two Contractors were being employed on various sites, and approximately 10,000 men were required. Subsequently, as the work proceeded, a further 12,000 were drafted. In this connection MrErnest Bevin, Minister of Labour, was extremely helpful It was found that, owing to the war, the building trade had been virtually disbanded; there were no scaffolders or steel fixers. I therefore arranged with Mr Bevin that he should make a demand on the Services for these skilled operatives and that they should be temporarily released from military service. There was considerable opposition to this from the Services, but when I pointed out that the Americans were unable to contribute, and that it would be undesirable at this stage to mix civilians and military labour owing to the differences in pay, agreement was reached and the men were drafted as civilians.

The difficulty of obtaining steel fixers seemed unsurmountable. I therefore arranged with Mr McCarthy, Superintendent of Conversion at the Admiralty, that 1,000 carpenters should be released from the Dockyards and that they should be trained to do this work because a skilled man can readily learn another trade. Fortunately Trades Union laws were elastic at this time. By this means the difficulties were solved.

Trade Unions laws were not elastic everywhere, however. John Laithwaite was involved with the construction of buffer pontoons, part of the Whale floating jetty:

I spent the last month of the construction period in charge of a small night shift — our job being to test each compartment as it was completed. I became expert at caulking small pin holes in weld metal with a diamond-pointed cold chisel. Unfortunately, if I so much as picked up a hammer on the day shift I was immediately challenged by the shop steward because I did not have a 'ticket' (trade union card). We had trade union troubles throughout the job — war or no war — and often finished up paying 10 shillings an hour to keep men working when there was a call to down tools for trivial complaints.

Major-General Wernher continues:

Over 30,000 tons of steel was required, but all the specially long railway wagons were in use in various parts of the country. It was accordingly necessary to mobilise every available wagon and divert it immediately to the steel mills in order that the necessary supplies could be brought to the sites.[6]

Concurrently with the *Mulberry* construction, the Admiralty were proceeding with an idea, invented by Lt.-Commander Lochner[7], for the constructions of the Bombardons. These were large steel tanks which were to be anchored outside the *Mulberry* in order to break the sea. I never had much faith in this invention, nor could I realise how it would be

[6] James Pope who worked for Mowlem on Phoenix construction remembers Sir Alan Harris, the engineer responsible for reinforcement, maintaining a large chart several yards long on his office wall at London's West India Docks. On it he recorded the precise state of the stock of every single bar.
[7] See Hickling's account on page 82.

possible to anchor these large Bombardons, which were some 200 ft. long.
Furthermore, it encroached on the slender steel supplies then available.
Eventually, when the severe storm came in June 1944, the *Bombardons*
came adrift and floated in all directions, breaking up quite a number of
craft.

In the story of Mulberry, the success or otherwise of the Bombardons seems to be a
contentious matter. As Vice Admiral Hickling stated earlier: '. . . By some miracle
they [the Bombardons] did not damage any ships as they drove ashore, nor did they
damage any of the breakwaters, as some people have stated.' And yet, Brigadier
Walter in the *Royal Engineers Journal* wrote: 'The Bombardon turned out to be a
disaster at both harbours. . . . In addition damage was caused by the Bombardons
which had broken their mooring in the storm.'

It is not perhaps surprising, however, that the Bombardons failed. They were
moored in deeper water than planned and were consequently less effective. They
withstood 30 hours of the storm that occurred on 19–23 June before breaking their
moorings in conditions where the stresses imposed were at least eight times as great
as the design stresses.

Major-General Wernher again:

> By this time, General Eisenhower had taken over the Supreme Command
> of SHAEF (Supreme Headquarters, Allied Expeditionary Force) [1943]
> and, on the first morning, he summoned all the Officers in the
> headquarters and addressed them in a manner which no one present will
> ever forget. He applied all his charm and personality and appealed for the
> utmost co-operation between the British and the Americans.
> Subsequently the senior Officers were taken into another room. He asked
> each of us in turn what we were doing and again addressed us. It was
> certainly a very good beginning to his Command. Meanwhile Field-
> Marshal Montgomery had arrived and taken over the Command of the
> Land Forces.
>   The Ministry of Supply were producing the pierheads and flexible
> roadways and some 250 contractors were being employed, Mr R A Davis
> being in charge. There was little doubt that this work would be completed
> on time, but the concrete construction was more difficult. I had an
> interview with Mr Bassett, Director of Docks. The Admiralty had been
> very forthcoming in allowing all the dry docks — eight in number —
> which were available to be placed at my disposal, except the Graving
> Dock at Southampton, which was required for the *Bombardons*, but these
> were insufficient and various improvisations had to be made. We decided
> to make our own docks on the banks of the Thames[8]. This necessitated

---

[8] See Hickling's account on page 84.

excavating and constructing basins the size of swimming baths behind
the banks of the River. The *Phoenix* was constructed up to a height of
eighteen feet, the banks were then broken down so that the water could be
let in, and the *Phoenix* floated up to other sites on the Thames to be
completed. The banks were then sealed up, the water pumped out and a
new *Phoenix* was started. At Stokes Bay, however, they were constructed
on slips and released into the water when completed.

The Prime Minister at this juncture intimated that in spite of my
reports, he was not sure that the task would be completed. Accordingly
all the Chiefs of Staff and American representatives, and those interested
in the project, were summoned to what we called 'The Midnight Follies',
namely a meeting starting at about 11 p.m. in the deep basement of the
Prime Minister's war headquarters in George Street, to discuss *Mulberry*
and the Blockships.

I knew, before the meeting, that one of the vital questions would be
the requisitioning of old ships to form blockships, (called *Gooseberries)* in
the shallow water thus saving the construction of *Phoenixes*; some sixty
to seventy would be required. I approached Sir Ralph Metcalfe, the
Director of Sea Transport, who said that, although the Battle of the
Atlantic was going well, he thought it would be difficult to find that
number of ships, even if the Americans were to produce half the quota.
However, I had taken the precaution of obtaining a list of all the old ships,
both in the Navy and the Merchant Service, and many of them were
unsuitable for post-war service. I accordingly suggested to Metcalfe that,
if these were requisitioned and paid for, it would be rendering a great
service to the shipping companies, who would thus be able to get rid of
their redundant and ancient ships. After the 1914/18 war, many old ships
of this type had been sold to the Greeks, who, because they had not the
same standards as those laid down by the Board of Trade, were able to
cut our prices in the Mediterranean and take away a lot of business from
British companies. This idea appealed to Metcalfe and, when we
assembled at the meeting, Mr Churchill stated that the requirement of
seventy ships had been asked for, but before sanctioning it, he must
consider whether this was an over-estimate, for he said, 'The Battle of the
Atlantic is going well but we cannot afford to take risks. I, personally,
have gone through the war without having a good lunch and I do not
wish to have to go without my breakfast'. To which Mr A V Alexander,
the First Sea Lord, replied that he would not be worried about breakfast
because he never took it. Whereupon Mr Churchill said, 'Am I to
insinuate from this, First Lord, that you do not come to until after lunch?'
This remark was greeted with hilarious laughter from all present.

The Prime Minister attended in a boiler suit, as usual smoking a
cigar, and asked a great many telling questions. It was clear from the

beginning that Admiral Cunningham, as a sailor, had grave suspicions of the whole project, and he proceeded to attack the War Office plan, which drew a reply from Brigadier Bruce White. Eventually, the Prime Minister, who was sympathetic towards the War Office, turned to Bruce White and said, 'The next time you attend a meeting, you had better turn up in blue'. Although Admiral Cunningham was a brilliant naval commander, he was not, in any sense, a staff Officer and strongly objected to the macabre ideas which were fostered by the Prime Minister. On the other hand, of the Chiefs of Staff, I found Lord Portal an outstanding figure, although Lord Alanbrooke was only a very little way behind him.

In order to reassure the Prime Minister, I did a tour of inspection with General Vaughan and he, with his technical knowledge, pointed out certain difficulties which must be overcome in order to expedite the job. The important factor was labour and, therefore, I went again to the Ministry and asked for an increased labour force, which was immediately forthcoming. It was, however, thought advisable to incite the men to speed up the work, a difficult matter in view of the security angle. The Prime Minister himself paid a visit to one of the sites, and later on Field-Marshal Montgomery went down to address the men working for McAlpine on the largest site in the East India Dock. This gigantic dock had been pumped out and ten *Phoenixes* were being constructed. After Montgomery had given a very nice address, I walked around in civilian clothes in order to discover the effect this had made. I heard one of the men remark, 'If we are such fine men as Montgomery says, why don't they give us more money?' Most of the labour was Irish and there were difficulties from time to time, and I remember speaking to one of the foremen of McAlpines, a Scotsman, who was incensed at the men being late. The foreman had obviously tumbled to the use to which these *Phoenixes* were to be put and said, 'I would like to tie a lot of these fellows on to the *Phoenixes* and let them go down when they sink them on the other side'.

At this time it was decided that all the *Phoenixes* should be fitted with anti-aircraft guns, and this made a further complication, both in the question of supply and construction. It turned out to be an unnecessary precaution because, by the time D-day arrived, the German air force had been virtually eliminated, and I doubt if the guns were ever used.

In the end, the proportions in which Phoenixes and Bombardons were used was determined by the availability of shipping for towing. The overall layout of the harbour was influenced by a number of other considerations. These were listed by John Jellet in his paper *The layout and assembly behaviour of the breakwaters at Arromanches Harbour (Mulberry B)* that appeared in the Institute of Civil Engineers' publication *The Civil Engineer in War (1948)*. In this paper he writes:

1) Meteorological information showed that the greatest protection was needed from north-west to north-north-west, that the Cherbourg peninsula would give considerable protection from west to north-west, and that the Le Havre peninsula and, at closer range, the Calvados shoal, would give similar protection from the north-east. Prolonged bad weather from the due north was unlikely and, in fact, was never encountered.

2) A tidal rise above LWST varying from 18 feet at neap tides to 24 feet at ordinary spring tides and as much as 26 feet at extraordinary springs was predicted. The existence of a strong coastwise current, westwards on the ebb and eastwards on the flood, with a stand of three hours at high water was also known. The strength of the current made it essential that the entrances should be so faced that ships would enter or leave on a course parallel to its direction and not across it.

3) It was necessary to give complete protection to the pierheads, the shore exits from which were almost rigidly determined by the layout of the roads serving the town of Arromanches, and which required to be in a least depth of 18 feet for use by coasters at all times. These conditions defined the position of the piers to within narrow limits.

4) The requirement to provide, if possible, anchorages for Liberty ships inside the harbour necessitated the enclosure within the breakwaters of a sufficient area having a least depth of 24 feet at LWST.

5) A blockship of 37 feet overall depth (the largest provided) placed in a depth of two fathoms would be submerged by one foot on a 26-foot tide. A ship of 25 feet overall depth (the smallest provided) would have to be placed in zero depth at LWST to be in similar conditions. The dimension taken to represent overall depth was the height from the keel to the highest continuous deck, and is a conservative one, making no allowance for bulwarks and superstructure, which have considerable value as part of the breakwater.

6) The overall depth of the largest caisson was 60 feet (it is doubtful if any larger unit could have been contemplated as a towing commitment), which would be comfortably submerged by a 26-foot tide if placed in a depth at LWST exceeding 34 feet, and objection to placing the units in such excessive depths lay in the possibility of disturbed conditions inside the harbour if bad weather should coincide with high spring tides. On the other hand, from the information available, there was a doubt whether the spacing of the seabed contours would allow the requirement (4) above to be met.

Like the pierheads, Phoenix construction was a colossal undertaking against an appallingly tight deadline. As Sir Alan Harris put it:

> The programme was enormous; hardly an indentation in the British
> coastline did not have some piece of Mulberry under construction. A list
> of those involved reads like a *Who's Who* of British construction. A
> contractors' committee was set up under Sir Malcolm McAlpine and
> certain simplifications in detail were insisted upon if the inexorable
> deadline was to be met. Some of these led to mishaps, such as some of the
> most exposed caissons having their walls broken outwards during the
> gale. The quality of their replacement is demonstrated by the fact that
> fourteen of these improved caissons remain intact in position in
> Arromanches today.

Seven firms or groups of consulting engineers were given responsibility for
supervising the construction of the caissons. These were Oscar Faber, Sir Alexander
Gibb & Partners, Sir Cyril Kirkpatrick, Rendel Palmer & Tritton, W T Halcrow &
Partners, Wolfe Barry Robert White & Partners and a group including Coode,
Mitchell, Vaughan-Lee and Gwyther.

Working on the Phoenix required, in some cases, considerable courage as work was
carried out at great heights over water. The schedule was punishing, with workers
sometimes working 'ghosters' — 48 hour shifts — to achieve deadlines. In London
and elsewhere there was also the ever present threat of bombing. Surprisingly, despite
the scale of the construction, the Germans did not seem to know what was going on.

At the Bovis site in Southampton water, a plumber, Dudley Wheeler, won a British
Empire Medal for bravery after saving a badly listing Phoenix, the result of concrete
being laid too quickly on one side of the unit. He shot down into the caisson and
opened some valves on the high side in an attempt to get it upright. Although
successful he was too late and the unit still sank, although it was later recovered
thanks to some quick thinking by Bovis' agent Jack Ward.

Jane Petrie recalls another incident which occurred near her battery at Gilkicker
Point near Gosport, Hampshire, where Phoenix units were built on the shore:

> Because, I presume, of tides, the units were built broadside on to the sea
> and had to be turned on rollers to be launched. Unfortunately, one had
> not 'set' properly and broke its back as it turned, crashing on to the men
> bearing the rollers. We were called on to help, and two of my ATS, Lance-
> Corporal Holford and Private Crowhurst, medical orderlies, were
> awarded the BEM for their sterling work under the ruin, with the tide
> coming in.

Allan Beckett was, as ever, in the thick of things and had a hand in getting Phoenix
construction off to a good start.

> Herbert Cruikshank, then Plant and Labour manager for Bovis, was rung
> in September 1943 by his managing director Paul Gilbert and told to be in
> Portsmouth at 9 a.m. the next day to organise some building work. . . .

Paul Gilbert was the old fashioned, purple complexioned sort of managing director. If he said to be there at 9 a.m. there was no question that I wouldn't be.

When I arrived there were 50 or 60 other contractors standing around outside the gate all asking each other what was going on. Eventually we were shown into a large room by a rating where we sat and waited. Suddenly another rating popped his head round the door. 'Please stand for the Admiral,' he said.

We all did, and for Paul Gilbert to stand for anyone was amazing. The Admiral stalked in wearing full dress regalia: hat, braid, everything. He looked at us and said: 'Gentlemen, I have been told that you are to come into My Dockyard to carry out important building work. I don't like it. I don't want you in My Dockyard but I am told your work is important. I expect you to behave in a responsible manner.' And off he went. Gilbert turned to me and said: 'Wonderful.'

He had recognised his twin.

We were then sent back to our offices with drawings provided by the MoD which we thought were of barges. There was nothing difficult about them, they were concrete structures, just massive and unusual ones. So I set about mobilising for the work and got the structures started in the drydock with the help of agent John Harvey. Nothing frightened him, not even Gilbert and not this job, though we were working in an atmosphere of incredible tension. I remember that very clearly.

In total, 147[9] caissons were constructed in eight wartime months; sixty at the largest size with a displacement of 6,044 tons. When it was all over, 330,000 cubic yards of concrete weighing 660,000 tons, 31,000 tons of steel and 1,500,000 super yards of shuttering had been required for their completion.

In the late spring of 1944, construction was drawing to a close and the components of the Mulberry harbour were to be towed to locations on the south coast and the Thames estuary before being organized for the big move to France.

Allan Beckett had first hand experience of the tows, as he explains:

They [Beetle pontoons] had to be towed to where the Phoenix units were assembled at Selsey. But the first two tows didn't arrive. I said to Bruce White: 'Shall I go on a tow?'

We didn't go very fast so I could lift the hatches and see in each of the six compartments. We came out of Spithead and turned left. There was a gate in the submarine netting. The first tow had to wait around while the tug opened the gate. I noticed it was not going through straight and got

---

[9] The final figure was 212

tangled up. We got through OK but they had holed one of the pontoons in the first tow. It promptly sank and soon they had all gone to the bottom.

I had no confidence in the concrete pontoons, we put timber baulks around them to protect them. Even so, I think there must be three miles of concrete pontoon bridging at the bottom of the Channel. I wrote an instruction manual but it had to be in guarded terms. The security was very well done by counter rumours such as: 'We were building a bridge across the Channel, but don't tell anyone.' The Germans knew we wouldn't go ashore on a rock-strewn beach.

Major-General Wernher was, as ever, required to fight his corner to acquire the necessary labour and resources required to complete his task:

During Easter week-end of 1944, I was disturbed about the arrangements being made by the War Office for the assembly of pierheads and floating roadways which were to be carried out at Marchwood, Southampton and Richborough. I therefore took Mr Gibson with me and he pointed out that the military labour employed was unlikely to achieve the results in time, as they were not organised in a businesslike manner. Furthermore, there were insufficient electricians to complete the work on the pierheads. I accordingly went to the Admiralty and to the Ministry of Supply to see whether we could mobilise any extra labour from these sources. Meanwhile I asked General Sir Humfrey Gale, who was the Chief Supply Officer at SHAEF, to summon a meeting. Before this I had been in touch with General Macmillan. He stated that everything possible was being done, but there were insufficient light cranes for the job. I asked him what steps he had taken to procure cranes and received an unsatisfactory reply. Before going into the meeting, I rang up the Ministry of Works and discovered that there were numerous cranes in the country which were being held in order to shift the coal which we had deposited in various dumps along the south coast. They stated that these could be moved at short notice if necessary.

At the meeting, General Macmillan stated his case, whereupon General Gale asked me for a solution. I denied General Macmillan's remark that cranes were not available and stated that, if I were given authority, I would guarantee to deliver the cranes in a short time. Furthermore, I stated that I had seen the Americans and, if necessary, they would place at our disposal a large number of Sea Bees (Marine Engineers). I also advised that if teams of Sea Bees and British Engineers were placed side by side, healthy competition would ensue. It was by this means that the equipment was all completed and assembled in time.

Apart from losses through sinking, there were some Phoenix units that failed to cross to France for other reasons, as Major Edwin Hunt recalls:

A number of Phoenix sections never made it to France because they could not be moved from the mud on which they had sat awaiting the call to Normandy. The phenomenon is known as 'sucking-down', when the mud will not release a barge on a rising tide. A number of riverside wharves were notorious as having mud of the right consistency for sucking-down. Barges destined for such wharves were never fully laden; instead they would carry perhaps 75 per cent of their potential to give them a chance of survival. The barge would be literally sealed in by the mud in which she had settled. The water could not get between the mud and barge to lift her up from it until the barge lifted up, so she stayed until the buoyant pressure built up and something had to give. Sometimes water would rise to deck level and above before she was free. Sometimes the barge stayed and her cargo was ruined. As an apprentice lighterman I was often sent to such a wharf to oversee a barge picking-up at night. At such times I was expected to poke away with a long hitcher at the adjoining mud to encourage water to suround her. If there was an empty barge nearby she would be used as a sort of battering ram to get things moving. When a barge broke free and rose up, sometimes as much as two feet, she would always give an audible warning — Marsh gas would be released from under her flat bottom as soon as she moved slightly, and this would gurgle to the surface with a loud bubbling noise.

I once saw a ship called *Philomel* at Mark Brown's Wharf jump up six feet, showing her wet mark six feet above the water line. In the course of my apprenticeship I met a lighterman who was a bosun at a notorious sucking-down wharf called Harland & Wolff's at Woolwich.When a barge arrived with a bit too much cargo this man would pass a wire hawser under her from side to side before she grounded. When the time came for her to pick up he would literally saw the barge free by working the wire to one end.

I have dwelt on this matter at some length to highlight the abysmal ignorance of those responsible for the safe keeping of these very important harbour walls. A hawser suspended beneath each Phoenix section amidships before grounding for the first time would have kept them free.

As Major-General Wernher's involvement with Mulberry drew to a close, the stiffest test of the floating harbour was about to begin.

At the beginning of May, 1944, it was clear to me that all the activities with which I had been entrusted were completed. I was not actually responsible for assembling the equipment, and the Admiralty had taken on the task of parking the *Phoenixes* until they were required. I therefore went to see General Ismay and told him that my duties were accomplished and that, as there was no other way in which I could contribute to the operation, I considered my appointment should be terminated.

SURVEY

We could see the posts in the light of the searchlight but then it went out and we were in total blackness. We went on slowly up the beach in darkness until the sergeant hit one of the poles with the mine detector. We knew then that it could not be a magnetic mine because it would have gone off.
— Lt. John Stone MC RE, recounting a daring mission to gather intelligence about D-day beach defences[10].

It was not, of course, possible to commence an undertaking of the size of Mulberry without knowing something of the conditions on the other side of the English Channel. For the D-day landings in general, an appeal was made for any reference information — postcards, holiday snaps — that would give an idea of the geography in and around Arromanches. For the civil engineers building Mulberry, however, more detail was required.

In his account of Mulberry, Vice Admiral Hickling says: 'The coast between Le Havre and Cherbourg — that is to say the Bay of the Seine — is not much frequented by mariners. . . . We sent out reconnaissance parties under Willmott and Berncastle, to mention but two of those gallant fellows who swam in at the dead of night in bitterly cold weather right under the noses of the German sentries to obtain the information we required'

In the following extract, General Scott-Bowden describes a reconnaissance sortie under Willmott, in this case not to obtain information for Mulberry but to find out details of the German beach defences and the load bearing capacity of the beaches. The personnel, craft, methods, location, risks, and dangers are identical to those for a Mulberry survey.

> As midget submarine X-craft 20 approached the Normandy coast shortly after dawn, cruising at 2½ knots on a southeasterly bearing, Commander Nigel Willmott DSO DSC RN, raised the periscope and said: 'There is a fleet of fishing boats just ahead!' Having successfully crossed the German minefield, passed the Pointe du Hoc, confirming our course, and rounded the Pointe de la Percée, this was an expected hazard. Our complement was Willmott, the head and founder of the Combined Operations Beach Reconnaissance and Assault Pilotage Parties, known as COPP, myself a major and Senior Military Officer of COPP, Lieutenant Ken Hudspeth

---

[10] From *Mission That Changed The Timing* — a reference to the D-day landings being switched from high to low tide owing to the presence of anti-tank mines on the beaches.

DSC RANVR (Royal Australian Naval Volunteer Reserve), the Captain from South Australia, Lieutenant Bruce Enzer RNVR (Royal Naval Volunteer Reserve), the Engineer Officer from Northern Ireland, and Sergeant Bruce Ogden-Smith DCM MM, formerly of the Special Boat Section, The East Surreys, and The Honourable Artillery Company.

We had left HMS *Dolphin* at Gosport on the morning of Monday 17 January 1944 and had unexpectedly been ordered to cross the Solent to call at the Royal Yacht Squadron, Cowes, where Willmott and I went ashore and received a short final updating on the operational situation and some words of advice and encouragement from Rear Admiral Sir Philip Vian VC, recently appointed to command of the British Invasion Fleet. We were then taken on tow by an armed trawler HMS *Darthema* and parted company with her well out into the Channel clear of our own minefields. We travelled on the surface using our diesel engine which was identical to those installed in London double-decker buses: in an X craft they are very smelly.

We had submerged off the French coast at dawn. The fishing boats ahead of us were all pointing southwest into wind with their nets out. Hudspeth, who had been in the attack which put the German Battleship *Tirpitz* out of action in Norway and knew the form on avoiding nets, recommended that we went under the bow of the nearest boat to avoid entanglement. Willmott agreed; then he saw there were armed soldiers on most boats presumably to prevent the French fisherman escaping in the night to England. I was on duty at the helm adjacent to the periscope and took a quick look hoping for a possible unit identification. The German soldier in the boat ahead was leaning back in the bow with a rifle slung over his shoulder and his greatcoat collar up: he was contentedly smoking a large curved cherry-wood pipe so I guessed he might come from Bavaria; there were no other clues. We passed under the little fleet and took a general view of the beach which we knew was to be for the Americans. It was nearly high tide when we beached at periscope depth in about 7 or 8ft of water on the left-hand sector of what was to be named 'Omaha' beach. Willmott took two bearings to fix our exact position and handed the periscope to me.

We had developed close inshore reconnaissance techniques off Kintyre in Scotland. It required much care to prevent exposure of bow or stern in the tidal waves. The trim needed frequent delicate adjustment by pumping water fore and aft. No one moved without the skipper's permission. The periscope was amazingly good although only about the thickness of a walking stick. Close inshore it could only be raised briefly about a foot to avoid detection, so it was important to come up on the correct bearing. Quite often when I was too absorbed in what was going on Willmott snapped: 'Down periscope!' He and I changed over regularly and took notes for each other. He also did thorough round-checks in case patrol craft were about. The early nightfall in winter stopped our fascinating viewing.

We withdrew offshore and then that first moment after surfacing when a hatch could safely be opened brought intense relief from the build-up of air pressure and shortage of oxygen. We moved out, still on the electric motor, far enough offshore to start the diesel where it could not be heard, for charging the batteries which took 3 to 4 hours. During this time, we had to listen to the BBC news. If it contained a certain phrase, that was an order to return to base immediately.

The batteries occupied almost the whole of the forward compartment leaving only about 2ft 6in maximum height for stowage of our COPP gear and in which to contort into our bulky swimsuits. Either Willmott or Hudspeth was up top on watch precariously and uncomfortably strapped to the raised air induction tube, now called a snorkel. Ogden-Smith and I prepared for the night reconnaissance while Enzer looked after everything else.

The lack of space in an X-craft whose maximum internal diameter is only 5ft. 11in is worth emphasis. Amidships under the main hatch is the tiny wet-and-dry compartment, so-called as it can be flooded to enable one swimmer at a time to leave or enter the X-craft under water. It also contains the heads which cannot be emptied in dangerous waters because of risk of detection! When using the wet-and-dry compartment underwater the swimmer has to operate the valves and pump as the water fills the compartment completely. The swimmer being partly buoyant is forced to the top. In the pitch dark you do not know whether you are on your head or your heels except by feel. It is the most unpleasant part of an X-craft crewman's training, but essential for their offensive role and in case of emergencies. Fortunately, on our operations we did not have to use this process as we could get out in reasonable weather conditions when the craft was surfaced. However, there is always a danger of taking in water even in a moderate sea.

Our personal COPP gear consisted of: identity disc; body-belt with escape aids, including photographs for identification papers which would be provided by the Resistance in case our recovery failed and if we made our rendezvous with them 12 miles inland; long johns; sweater; swimsuit hood and fitted boots; webbing belt; Colt 45 automatic and spare magazines, commando knife; cutters; wrist compass; wristwatch; emergency ration; waterproofed directional torch to signal for recovery and an 18in earth auger for testing bearing-capacity. There were many variations to these depending on the operation and climate. Bearing in mind that those special Royal Marine Commandos who had been captured after their brilliant raid at Bordeaux under Colonel 'Blondie'

Haslar in December 1942 were all executed under Hitler's orders, I insisted that our badges of rank were sewn onto our swimsuits and sweaters so that if caught it could be seen we were not disguising the fact that we were soldiers. The Intelligence Staff had warned us that if captured we would probably be taken straight to Paris for very subtle interrogation, initially by the armed forces.

The batteries were charged and Ogden-Smith and I were ready for the night reconnaissance ashore on the left-hand sector which was to become the United States 1st Division beach. There was a moderate sea, some cloud, and so conditions were good. We were able to move in close on the electric motor to shorten the swim. There was about 300yds of exposed beach above the rising tide. Nevertheless, remembering how soldiers had been about earlier, we were cautious. We had selected a stretch of beach away from buildings and possibly sentries. Fortunately, we were not required to bring back any samples from the beach itself, as we were by now, as a result of an earlier reconnaissance, trusted by the scientific experts to be able to check accurately the beach-bearing-capacity wherever we went. We covered quite a large area of beach and fortunately when we were examining the shingle bank below the wire and the road where there was some cover, we heard what we thought was probably an inattentive two-man patrol talking and moving east. We swam out beyond the breakers; our recovery went smoothly, and we moved well out to charge batteries. While that was happening we had to take everything off, check, and store all our kit, clean our Colt 45 automatics which we stripped on top of the echo sounder. Then there was a very welcome sort of brew-up produced by Enzer. Little of the night remained. We dived at dawn and moved in for a repeat performance on the right hand sector towards Vierville which was to become the United States 29th Infantry Division beach. Daylight reconnaissance went well revealing much detail of the work in progress and we prepared for another night's sortie.

Although it was mid-January, the sea had become very calm, a condition we did not like at all as even when the moon is down anything moving on the surface can be seen from a long way off. We slid off the casing several hundred yards out and swam quietly into shallow water crawling forward slowly about 400yds east of the Vierville re-entrant observing and listening when suddenly a powerful torch was beamed straight at us. We did not move, kept our faces down and took care to keep aligned with the beam as the gently rising tide could swing us broadside showing our shapes. The sentry did not approach, but he kept his torch trained firmly on us. In time as the tide came in we eased gently back. He then swung his beam about and eventually switched if off. I have often wondered what he thought he had seen and whether he reported it? We then swam well to the east and tried again. This time there was no trouble.

We examined the beach with our augers over a wide area as planned, and the shingle bank at the back of the beach, made mainly of rounded stones about 6in in diameter. Whilst we were ashore a Bomber Command raid had been laid on in the River Orne area to divert sentries' attention. Surprisingly the flashes from successive bomb explosions many miles away lit up the X-craft well out to sea. It was very visible to us on shore and that was disturbing. We crawled back knowing our tracks would be erased by the tide, swam in the calm sea about half a mile out before signalling for recovery. We completed the night's routine, keeping very alert to crash dive while surfaced for battery charging. Next morning we closed in on the Vierville sector again, hoping to find out more about the defences. After raising the periscope briefly a few times, strange external rather unpleasant clanging noises started. Willmott soon saw small shells exploding close to the periscope. Had we been detected? We thought not. We were moving very slowly at about half a knot, with the small stick-like periscope exposed, at intervals, about a foot only. As it was not disturbing the water, perhaps it was thought to be a stray mine and was being used as a good aiming mark for target practice. The shooting had gone on intermittently for about 20 minutes without damaging the periscope. We would have been blinded if it had been hit.

Although prepared to do a third night's reconnaissance, we had already acquired a mass of information, so there was little point in staying around taking an unnecessary risk as, if our presence had been suspected, a search by patrol craft or even aircraft, which might see us in the shallow water, were possibilities. We headed for home. Next day *Darthema* spotted us and escorted us towards Portsmouth harbour with two Motor Gun Boats (MGBs). We made fast alongside the jetty in the inner harbour of HMS *Dolphin* where to our surprise Rear Admiral Dark commanding the submarine base and a few others were waiting to receive us. When the rear hatch was opened setting up a through draught, there was a slight onshore breeze. It was amusing to see the reception committee recoil from the X-craft's four days of accumulated odours.

With all the information that was available, a large model of each harbour was built in great secrecy. In the run up to D-day only a few, directly concerned senior officers saw the models. And, as [Vice] Admiral Hickling has written: 'On these models with movable pieces many "games of chess" had to be played before the best lay-out of the harbour was arrived at. It was indeed remarkable how closely the finished harbour followed the final arrangement of this model.'

TRANSPORTATION

Never was I more proud of the title 'Master of the Merchant Navy and Fishing Fleets' than at the time of the Normandy landings when thousands of merchant seamen, in hundreds of ships, took across the Channel on that great adventure our armies and their equipment.

Never was pride better justified. This was the greatest combined operation the world had ever seen — perhaps the greatest it will ever see. The three fighting services and the Merchant Navy worked as one vast, complex, but perfectly constructed machine and won a resounding victory.

— HM King George VI in his Christmas message, 1944

King George's pride was indeed justifiable. By the Spring of 1944 all the vast, component and innumerable complex parts (which have already been described in some detail in Chapters 3 and 4) of Mulberry were complete and ready to be transported from places all over the UK, where they had been constructed. They were to be towed to Southampton for final fitting before being taken across the Channel and assembled on the French coast, creating harbours each bigger than that at Dover, (which is also artificial, but was constructed in peace-time, without rush, and without an opposing enemy attempting its destruction).

Nothing of such size and weight had ever been towed in this manner before, and, although trials had been made using scale models in tanks of water, it was by no means certain that these would provide an accurate assessment of performance of the actual units in the waters of the Channel.

But, even before this could begin the parts had to be assembled from all the different areas of the UK where they had been constructed.

Major-General Sir Harold Wernher, in overall charge of the Mulberry construction, was ultimately responsible for solving all of the various problems which beset the construction, assembly, launching and gathering in to Southampton of all the various parts of the harbour. As always, in solving these, he displayed not only his ability to delegate, but his unerring choice of the right men to handle the job.

> As the time was now approaching when the *Phoenixes* were to be launched on the south coast site, it became necessary to mobilise dredgers from the Clyde, because the approaches to the beaches had become silted up during the war. There was a great shortage of dredgers at this time but, largely owing to the assistance of Mr R P Biddle, who was then at the Ministry of Transport, and with American co-operation, this question was solved.
>
> Mr Biddle, the Docks and Marine Manager, Southampton, had always been a most co-operative member of the CMSF. Committee.

There was no obstacle which he failed to overcome in the shortest space of time, and he had ways and means of carrying out the most difficult tasks, I have no doubt with very little reference to his senior Officers. His pre-war appointment had enabled him to know a great many people in the field of transport and, with his cheerful personality, there is no doubt that he prevailed upon them to carry out his wishes.

The launching of single parts to begin their voyage of assembly did not always prove simple. Thomas Coughtrie gives a graphic account of two incidents of this kind. The first occurred with the launch of a pierhead into Lochryan in Wigtownshire. Thomas Coughtrie travelled to Stranraer by train, to be met by his assistant Peter.

Cairnryan again, with Peter once more to meet me at Stranraer Station. Peter's news was good, all was going splendidly and a launch was arranged for later in the week. This was to be a grand occasion and everyone was on tenterhooks, hoping that all would be well. Indeed, it was an occasion to be heightened by the presence of the Colonel-in-Chief who had been persuaded to ask his staff and their Ladies to attend. A kind of grandstand was built above the launch pad so that they could see well and also be given a little protection if the weather proved to be dirty. Everybody worked like demons to make sure that all went well. But Peter was worried. His experiences reminded him that, on many occasions, vessels proved to be reluctant to move towards their new element, the sea. On Clydeside, heaps of soft soap and tallow and grease were spread on the rails to facilitate movement. This movement could, indeed, prove precipitate once it was started and great lengths of very heavy chains and ropes and weights were hooked to the vessel to check its speed. So, at Cairnryan, there were those who had fears; there were also those who were born optimists; and they were all outnumbered by a host of well-wishers among the pierhead's builders who were determined that all would go well.

The great day dawned with welding still going on apace! The launching crews had improvised astonishingly and nothing was left undone to ensure the success of the occasion. In due course, the official party assembled. Peter took his place among the VIPs but I stayed on board the pierhead. At the moment of high tide, the signal was given and the chocks were hammered away — but the 'Darling' slept on! There was no explanation for her reluctance and, after 15 or 20 minutes, fears began to be expressed about an ebbing tide. Suddenly a very stout wooden stump was found to have embedded itself between the rocks and the vessel. There was quick talk of using explosives to move it as it was stuck hard. Amazingly, when a wire rope was attached and hooked to the Derrick, it was pulled sidewise and the pierhead raced, like a greyhound, into Loch Ryan. All was well, the pierhead was captured by a tug and those on board, who hadn't taken my warnings seriously, were rubbing their bruises — 1,000 tons, 200 feet long meeting resistance of a wall of water creates quite a shock. There were hasty examinations to seek for leaks and occasional buckled plates but only a few bothers came to light and there she was – gorgeous. Everyone cheered and cheered!

Peter told me that, as he stood near the Colonel and it was known that the last impediment had been found and was about to be moved after the anxious wait, a Sergeant (known to everyone as a 'Dodger' — a fanatical glory seeker) sprang in front of the CO. and, saluting smartly, announced: 'The pierhead is all ready now and is about to be launched, Sir!' The CO's reply shook those near enough to hear it: 'Bugger Off!' he said, and the Sergeant slunk away. The Sergeant was the only Royal Engineer I know who could ever have been faulted.

Almost immediately after this successful launch, an emergency arose at Faslane. Thomas, who had travelled from Lochryan to the Gareloch via Newhaven in Fife to inspect the readiness of other, completed Whales, returned to Headquarters Office at Clydesmouth. Next morning he received an urgent summons to the Chief's office. He takes up the tale himself

I found him slightly agitated (which was not usual at all) and standing! The questions started before I had the door shut: 'Where's your report on the last Whale at Faslane?'. I said that it was on his desk and made to fetch it, only to be stopped and told not to bother with that now. I was asked if all the equipment was in order, tested thoroughly and working, to which I replied in the affirmative. Then I found out why all the anxiety: a forward winch could not be operated. I at once said that if I could use the telephone I could, with a few queries, identify the reason and suggest an immediate remedy (all this with fingers crossed). On top of this I was told that the Whale in question was booked for the imminent tide and that the tugs and escort were already on hand and everyone was waiting. 'I'm sure I can tell' was as far as I got, then 'the Naval Officer in Command has specifically asked for you, there is a car waiting at the front entrance with a driver who has been told to get you to Faslane at once. Get moving and telephone me as soon as you can'.

Thus ensued a pleasant journey on almost empty roads, undertaken at interesting speed by a well-spoken lady driver. I was expected, so the car shot through the Command Post and on down to the Quayside. Dismounting, and walking smartly (taught never to run or show anxiety) I shot down the gangway and through a crowd of expectant 'no-hopers', to the panel under the deck. It had been expected that I would look at and examine the recalcitrant and reluctant winch, but my experience took me to the control. In less time than it takes to tell, I found the trouble. It was a stuck overload trip lever, the bearings of which had been corroded by salt water. I cleaned them and begged for some oil — none was forthcoming, so I got the cook to provide some grease and used it instead. 'Try that', I called, switching on, and in a few seconds, the offending winch obeyed its commands and ran sweetly. Back again on the deck with a final look at the winch (as a gesture only) I turned and went back ashore, to report to the Naval Officer in Command, and to telephone the Chief. On coming out of the Office, I saw the last Whale set off on its journey into the history books as the tug's sirens woke up the sirens of all the other vessels in the port. And so, a last page was closed on Scotland's story of its contribution to the Harbour so diligently sought for by the Prime Minister and so wonderfully achieved and fulfilled by some splendid master strokes of vision, design, ingenuity, manufacture and sheer determination.

Thomas Coughtrie had successfully launched all the Whales with which he was concerned. Launching achieved, towing began, and, as has already been described by previous writers, this brought its own problems.

> In the late spring, some of the equipment was being completed and it became necessary to tow the pierheads to Southampton for assembly from the various points up the coast of England. This was a hazardous task, undertaken at night, but all arrived safely at Southampton where they were to be fitted up with various electrical equipment. The *Phoenixes* were all being towed down the Thames where they were to be parked until required, when unfortunately the Naval Officer in charge of one, took a wrong sounding, and the *Phoenix* was sunk out of sight and was, therefore, never seen again.

In the meantime, Allan Beckett was exploring the problem of towing unwieldy sections of bridge spans. He had, at first, thought of mounting the bridge spans on adapted Thames lighters, but it rapidly became clear that not nearly enough lighters would be available. Beckett had to design a new type of float for the bridge. He explains his solutions to some of the problems that he encountered when the coupled floating bridges set out on their journeys to the assembly area at Selsey.

> With regard to the flotation of the bridge spans, other more pressing uses were found for Thames lighters. Many were converted to a form of landing craft called a Power Boat Ramp. I was therefore asked to design the ideal float for the bridge. The steel beetle was the outcome. It had a shape designed to minimise pitching yet had plenty of strength for pounding on a hard beach in surf conditions. The beetle pontoon was compartmented and had independent sections that were bolted together, and thus permitted different pontoon lengths. Each section was air-pressure-tested at the works to ensure water tightness. There was

produced a reinforced concrete alternative, but I was not happy with it as it seemed to me to be less suitable for the rough and tumble of military use at sea.

Much of my time was devoted to the means by which the floating bridge (by this time codenamed 'Whale') could be assembled and positioned on the enemy coast. There were of course the problems of towage across a hundred miles of open sea with a long fetch from the Atlantic Ocean, and the limitation on the number of tugs available to make and repeat the round trip, and transport not only floating bridge units, but pier head spud pontoons, various types of intermediate pontoons, concrete breakwaters, floating steel breakwater units and blockships.

The first scheme devised for the coupling of the floating bridges involved a system of tows in each of which one bridge span linked two pontoons and carried a second span on top. Thus a two-span length of bridge comprised a single tow. This system was tested at Cairn Head by Major Tonks and his 970 Floating Equipment company. Assembly at site was by no means simple, easy or quick and the idea was discarded. A naval officer watching the operation with me suggested that I might think about using a Camel — a pontoon in which buoyancy can be changed. I had not considered it but from that moment on could think of little else as a solution to this assembly problem. Eventually an erection tank or form of Camel was evolved, and with it the trumpet-shaped locators that allowed one six span tow to be coupled up to another in just twenty minutes, given any sort of reasonable weather. This meant that a mile-long pier could be positioned and moored up in about four hours as long as we had sufficient tugs to bring the tows across Channel .

The manufacture of so much bridging in so short a time put great strain on the British steel fabricators, yet the objective was achieved, very much through the skill of Col. P K Benner in the Ministry of Supply. The bridge components were made in small pieces by firms all over the country, some of them developing expertise in precision fabrication by welding that had previously not been thought possible. Assembly of these components into fully fitted operational tows by army units took place at Richborough under Lt. Col. Holmwood RE and at Marchwood under Lt. Col. Stork RE. Because Richborough had limited depth of water, only tows using steel pontoons could be assembled there.

It was by now proving impossible to produce sufficient steel plate to meet both the demand for steel beetles and the Navy's floating breakwater 'Bombardon', and my objection to concrete was therefore overruled and a form of concrete beetle, having thin walls 1.25" thick but still very heavy, was introduced. It was to be positioned only where depth of water ensured it would not ground on the sea bed. All the concrete beetles were made at Marchwood and formed the floats for the flexible spans assembled in that depot. The tows, when fully assembled, were to be towed to and moored in assembly areas more or less in the shelter of the Isle of Wight. This required a substantial coastwise journey for the units assembled at Richborough though not of course for those assembled at Marchwood.

However there must have been some problems with the Marchwood tows because although they left Marchwood they failed to arrive at the Selsey assembly area and several of them had disappeared completely en route[11].

I was sent to find out what had happened and joined one of the newly finished tows at Marchwood with another that left just before us and we departed together for the assembly area. I asked our tugmaster what he thought of his tow. His reply was that he hoped he would not be asked to tow anything like this across the Channel!

On the journey I inspected each of the six pontoons and found them perfectly watertight. I was thoroughly mystified about the disappearing tows, until we approached the gate through the submarine defence, whereupon a concrete beetle at the first tow seemed to get entangled with it. After extrication, this leading tow went ahead but was slowly sinking, and, like its predecessors, sank before it reached its destination. In the case of my own tow greater care was taken in negotiating the gate and we were the first of the tows to arrive at Selsey from Marchwood without damage. I remained convinced that for military equipment, subject to rough handing in maritime conditions, something more robust than thin walled concrete was required. My report to War Office was not well received. It was known that I disliked the concrete beetles and it was considered too late to make a change in plan. The chosen answer was to increase the number of spare concrete beetle pontoons. This seemed to me to be treating the floating bridge as well as its concrete pontoon supports as lavishly expendable. The American Construction Battalion (Sea Bees) took a different view and put in hand the replacement of their concrete beetles by an adaptation of their steel NL pontoon equipment. Such modified Floating Bridge tows found their way into Mulberry A and later on into Mulberry B after the storm of D+13.

The assembly of tows with steel pontoons at Richborough also had problems. Due to the limited slack water period at high tide it became difficult to load all six shuttles on board each of the six span tows, and dispensation from War Office was obtained to send off the tows with only one mooring shuttle aboard.

---

[11] See Beckett's account on page 91

Reports such as Beckett's underline not only the problems which arose, but the completely innovative nature of the work which they were undertaking, and the skill and ingenuity they brought to deal with each successive difficulty as soon as it became apparent.

As we saw earlier, another problem facing Major-General Sir Harold Wernher was the requisitioning of sufficient blockships for the purpose of the Gooseberry component of the Mulberry breakwater. Sir Harold got his blockships, though the argument he used to acquire them was certainly not the one envisaged by Vice Admiral Hickling in his account of what might have happened at the meeting. Market economy, not patriotism won the day!

It was on one of the old ships, which was in fact a Greek boat, that Owens Elliot from Stranraer sailed, as he says 'one night near 6th June 1944'. This was his story.

> I took part in making Mulberry Harbour.
>
> This battalion of Gunners were on duty in Ceylon and were ordered home in February for Special Duties.
>
> We arrived at Greenock and were despatched to Paisley. From there we went to Leith to a Naval Gunnery School for special training on ack-ack Guns. On finishing the course, we were taken to Destination Unknown.
>
> When we arrived it was dark and we were put onto small ships at Methil, Fife and transferred to old merchant ships, one corporal and five marines to each. The ship I was on was a Greek boat with Captain and skeleton crew and five ack-ack guns, and it was our job to man those guns. We were told we would be sailing to a Destination Unknown, so one night near 6th June 1944, we set sail with this great armada of old ships. When our destination was reached, we found we were anchored off Poole.
>
> On June 19th, Admiral Ramsay commanding the Naval element of the Invasion Force, as the weather was good, set sail for France with a great force of boats, bridges and barges to make the breakwater and Mulberry Harbour. This floating roadway would eventually provide seven miles of flexibility within the Mulberry Harbour.
>
> I can tell you, this was a great experience to take part in, I will never forget what we felt like when we discovered our mission, as these boats were all primed with explosives to scuttle them. We called ourselves 'the suicide squad'.

How very pleasant it is that he survived to tell his remarkable story.

This loss of a Phoenix makes no mention of anyone who was actually aboard it when it sank. Harold Boyle had a much more traumatic experience when the Phoenix he was travelling on broke adrift. His brother, W J Boyle of Millom in Cumbria, tells the story, and adds a fascinating post-script to it.

My brother (now deceased) Able Seaman Harold Boyle and a soldier were travelling on a Phoenix caisson which was being towed down to the South Coast. A storm got up off the Cornish coast, and the thing broke adrift. A lifeboat eventually came and took them off, but jumping into the lifeboat, my brother hurt his ankle and had to spend some time in hospital. He always said he thought there was not one man under the age of 70 years on that lifeboat. Needless to say he was always grateful to them.

He said to me when he knew I was going on holiday to Cornwall, to visit some lifeboat stations, as he had no idea which boat had taken them off. Well, after visiting a few stations, I found it and there on the wall at Clovelly boat station was:

19th October 1944[12] caisson Phoenix No.193
Clovelly Life Boat 'The City of Nottingham' launched and
saved 8. Re-launched and gave help

Sapper J McKenzie of Edinburgh was serving in the 962 Port Construction and Maintenance Company when he first encountered the Mulberry Harbour. Stationed at the village of Sandwich in Kent, where they put together the floating part of the bridge, he was picked out with five others to go to the War Office in London and subsequently to go on a Phoenix caisson to France. He recalls what followed his arrival at the War Office:

We were taken to a room, and on the table was a model about 2 ft long and 1 ft wide. It was divided into six or eight departments. There was a small steering-wheel-like thing with a long stem reaching about near the bottom, and a larger one not so far down. We were told the small wheel was to open the small valve first, after that we were to open the larger valve. . . . After the lecture we asked the officer what it was for, but he would not tell us.

The day after, . . . we were taken to a very large building where there was a huge water tank with a moveable gantry on top. . . . I can't tell you when or which part of the Channel we left from, because it was at night and very dark, nor do I know which part of France we landed on. I did not get my feet wet. I remember getting transport so far, then we had a force march the rest of the journey, again it was dark. We were told to dig a trench and make ourselves comfortable. It was only in the morning that we were told that we were actually in Arromanches.

Returning to Major-General Wernher's account and his part in the transportation and assembly of the pierheads and floating roadways, we find him still struggling to

---

[12] This Phoenix was sunk four months after D-day, which illustrates that Phoenixes were still needed for repair and replacement, since Mulberry was designed to be used for 100 days.

acquire both manpower and machinery to complete the task. He was especially concerned by the shortage of trained engineering personnel. This was supplemented by a most generous and timely offer from the Americans. They promised Sir Harold that

> If necessary, they would place at our disposal a large number of Sea Bees (Marine Engineers). I also advised that if teams of Sea Bees and British Engineers were placed side by side, healthy competition would ensue. It was by this means that the equipment was all completed and assembled in time.

Sir Harold here makes the first mention of the American Marine Engineers who were popularly known as Seabees. These were, in fact the 108th Naval Construction Battalion which had arrived in England in November 1943, and who had received intensive training in the spring of 1944 in the transport, assembly and eventual setting up and organising Omaha, the American harbour. More of the Seabees story will be told later in this account.

Despite this additional and welcome support, the actual assembly at Southampton began to fall behind schedule because of the sheer magnitude of the task.

Guy Hartcup, author of *Code Name Mulberry* explains what happened next

> It was not surprising that the contractors failed to keep to schedule. The first batch of RE Equipment, in the Ministry of Supply, was responsible for organising the manufacture of machinery and equipment for the spud pontoons. Appreciating the anxiety of the Chiefs of Staff and Overlord planners, R D Davis, the Deputy Director-General, addressed a meeting of the British Structural Iron Association in London during the first week of April. The response was immediate. A force of 300 welders from various firms was rapidly assembled under the direction of Dorman Long at Southampton. They had no knowledge of the work they had to do except that it was vital and desperately urgent. The first five pierheads were completed by 10th May, and according to Davis, 'saved the situation'.

The large, new force of welders, together with commandeered welding sets and mobile cranes, allowed the work to go ahead with speed. Not all the pierheads were complete in time to cross the channel on D-day, but, as events were to prove, there were enough to do the job. Guy Hartcup finishes his story

> When each pontoon was completed in detail it was tested and alternately crewed with British (969 port Construction and Repair Co.) or Americans from 108 Construction Battalion. The Americans were usually in charge of chief petty officers, many of whom had been oil drillers in Texas and were knowledgeable and highly competent in their work. The pontoons were then towed away to anchorages in the Solent off Selsey. Three

pontoons were fitted out at Woolwich and Falmouth. The story is told of the naval look-outs at Dover who had reported a strange-looking object in the distance undulating through the water like a sea serpent. It proved to be a bridge tow, low in the water, the spans sticking above the horizon, en route to Selsey.

By mid-May, fourteen pierheads were on tow or had arrived at Southampton, leaving one outstanding for the initial requirement. All the pierheads bar one were completed before the end of June, though four of them still had to be fitted with spuds.

All these stories of towing successes, disasters, and disasters just averted have, so far, ignored the force by which the vast pieces of equipment were collected at Southampton. This omission is made good in excerpts from *Shipyard Spotlight* of November 1944

" — and the Tugs were there too!"

In February and March of this year, when people were still chalking 'Second Front' on the walls of back streets, tugs wearing the White and Red Ensigns, all around our coasts, were called in from their everyday war duties to go on a mission. This turned out to be the biggest job of their careers.

They went to ports and estuaries all over the country and from yards operated by engineers and building contractors, towed southwards various ungainly components of the now-famous prefabricated harbours which made it possible for us to supply the Allied armies landed in France on D-day and the period immediately following. They took their charges round to the south coast ready for the signal that was to take the strangest convoy in history across the English Channel.

Queer Names

The components had all sorts of queer names like 'gooseberry', 'mulberry', and 'phoenix' with models of which towing trials had been made in advance in the testing tanks at the National Physical Laboratory at Teddington.

The large units of the prefabricated harbours weighed 6,000 to 7,000 tons and required our highest-powered tugs to move them along at a reasonable speed. Sometimes two tugs worked with a bridle.

The tugs had towed the heaviest invasion equipment ever known into position. Now all waited for June 5th, D-day. By 3rd June, the advance weather forecast was very bad for 5th June. The Commanding Officers under the Supreme Command of General Eisenhower held discussions on both 3rd and 4th of June. General Montgomery was determined to stick to the originally decided date of 5th June. Air Marshal Sir Trafford Leigh-Mallory, Commander of the Allied Expeditionary Air Force, seemed unable to make a decision. Air Chief Marshal Sir Arthur Tedder,

Deputy Supreme Commander, felt dubious of Eisenhower's choice of 6th June. Finally, at 9.45 p.m. of the 4th June, General Eisenhower overrode all the objections and ordered the operation to start on the 6th.

The men of all forces, cooped up in their transports or crowded into temporary barracks were unaware of the change of date, but only too aware of the stress of waiting, and tension rose.

Across in France, members of the resistance had been listening to the BBC's broadcasts to the French Resistance, fully aware of the dangers they faced if they were caught in this 'treason' to the Government. On the 1st June, those listening heard the pre-arranged signal of imminent invasion read out; three lines of Verlaine's *Chanson d'Automne*

> Les sanglots longs
> Des violons
> De l'automne

It had been arranged that, when the last three lines of the verse were read, and they were expected on the 4th June, the invasion would take place within the next twelve hours. The 4th June came and the lines were not read. The members of the French Resistance were aware of the postponement. Then on the 5th June, they came

> Blessent mon coeur
> D'une langueur
> Monotone.

and the Resistance prepared to harry and obstruct the German defenders in every way they possibly could.

The invasion force was led by a flotilla of mine-sweepers, clearing the way for the troops, and for the floating harbour, together with the men who were to assemble it. They were given the signal by Admiral Sir Bertram Ramsay on 5th June, and the press regarded the response as a lucky sign. They reported the departure a few days later.

The *Shipyard Spotlight* for November 1944 reported a further co-incidence in this event. HMS *Pelorus* had been built by Lobnitz & Co., of Renfrew who were also responsible for designing the Spud Pontoon Pierheads of Mulberry.

Attempting to follow the exact schedule of those who described their actions in the invasion is complicated. Some give precise dates of embarkation and eventual landing in Normandy; others give a sequence of events without ascribing dates to them. From the accounts received, and from which this narrative is constructed, the first to embark seems to have been Brigadier A E M Walter, appointed to command the British Mulberry B Port Construction Force (PCF) which, in his own words, 'carried out the Army's task of planting the harbour on the beach at Arromanches'. 'This', as he says, 'was the last link, the final cornerstone of this great project'. The different RE units which made up the PCF 'only came together for the first time on D-day +1 (7th June) when they began to arrive at Arromanches. He gives a very clear account of his own responsibilities in the assault

> As Director Ports & IWT[13] 21 AGp[14] my responsibilities in the assault included:
>
> (a) The planting and operation of the British artificial harbour at Arromanches.
> (b) The discharge of stores, ammunition, vehicles, etc, from ships to all the beaches.
> (c) The repair and operation of the small ports of Port-en-Bessin on the right flank of the British Sector and of Ouistreham on the left and the clearance of Ouistreham-Caen canal as a supply route and of Courselles.
>
> To achieve (a), as explained above, a special Port Construction Force was organised under Colonel S K Gilbert consisting of two Port Floating Equipment (PFE) Companies RE — 969 and 970 the combined companies being under command of Lt. Colonel Ronnie Cowan, their task being to plant the floating piers and to build the floating roadways which connected them to the shore. No 1 Port Construction & Repair (PC&R) Group RE — commander Lt. Colonel Donald May with 935 PC&R Company RE (Major Hinricks) responsible for the demolitions and engineering works ashore. No 5 PC&R Group RE — commander Lt. Colonel Homewood with 930 PC&R Company RE responsible for crewing and sinking the concrete caissons.
>
> From memory I think the total RE Transportation strength in the Order of Battle on D-day was around 7,000 all ranks of which only three RE Officers besides myself were Regular Army.
>
> To carry out this task, the Directorate of Ports and IWT 21 AGp was organised under me as follows:
>
> DD Tn Construction — my deputy Colonel (Daddy) A E Howarth — a distinguished civil engineer with an excellent record in WWI. He had general responsibility for all port engineering and I leaned on his experience heavily.
>
> DD Tn Port Construction Force — Colonel S K Gilbert — mentioned above. He also was an experienced civil engineer with a lively and unorthodox mind, which was not fully appreciated at times by the sailors.
>
> DD Tn Port Operating — Colonel Tommy Thompson — mentioned above. I had met him before the war when he was in the Supplementary

---

[13] Inland Water Transport
[14] 21 A Group

Reserve to which Transportation RE owed so much when war came. If ever anyone knew his job and could lead, it was Tommy Thompson.

DD Tn IWT Operating — Colonel 'Slim' Bowen — a master at his job whom I only really got to know on the beaches and later in the campaign.

AD Tn — Personal Deputy — Lt. Colonel Raymond Mais. He got into the act in April 1944 even later than I did. He came from Combined Operations and was sent around to get to know as much as possible about the PCF units which were unfortunately still under War Office control at that date. He was one of those ideal invaluable officers to have around who find out all about everything, ears firmly to the ground; shoot trouble, get things done and are born leaders close to all ranks. I was lucky to have him and later he became godfather to one of my sons. Later still he became Lord Mayor of London.

As the planting of the harbour was thought to be vital to the success of the landings, it was decided that until about D+20 I would establish my HQ at Arromanches and that the building of the harbour would be my first daily personal task during that time.

This large force only came under command of 21 AGp at the eleventh hour, much much too late for safety, especially in the case of the PCF in which some units had never even seen the equipment, and never trained with it until they arrived on the beaches.

Sometime early in April I had had to know the exact location of the harbour but early in May I had to be told the planned date of D-day. This was a great burden especially after my lapse of security and I was even scared of babbling in my sleep.

For the last week before D-day, my HQ moved to some rather nice empty houses down by the shore at Selsey. We took with us from Norfolk House the large model of the harbour at Arromanches — today I am told it is on display in the Mulberry museum at Arromanches and no doubt one has to pay the French to see it! We were very worried at having it down there on the shore in case we were attacked, and so, in addition to the permanent guards, the bravest of the clerks were assigned to die destroying the model at all costs if attacked.

Brigadier Walter embarked on his mission on 3rd June, but joined the invading convoy on D-day itself. He takes up the story:

> On Saturday 3rd June — D-3 as it turned out to be, the main party of HQ PCF embarked on HMS *Aristocrat*, a shallow-draught Clyde paddle steamer (in peacetime well known as the *Talisman*) and the remainder of us boarded on D-2. On D-day HQ PCF came into operation and the first signal was made to Rear Admiral Mulberry/Pluto (Rear Admiral

Tennant) at 1410 hours and we moved to our position in convoy at 1430 hours.

We arrived at our station off shore at Arromanches before dawn on D+1. At first light, to our consternation, we saw German soldiery through glasses on the high ground to the west of the town. This meant that right at the start our plans were adrift because it had been planned that Arromanches should be liberated by units of 231 Brigade on D-day so that the PCF units could begin to move in unopposed on D+1 and start on the very tight schedule of planting the harbour. However, a little later, the Survey Launch *Javelin* with Raymond Mais and Lieutenant Ashton came alongside to report. Mais had landed on D-day and was responsible for establishing the in-shore and off-shore markers for the floating piers and reconnoitring the beach exits and seeing that the in-shore hydrographical survey was done. The Sappers were responsible for the in-shore survey from the four-fathom line at low water while the Navy was responsible for the offshore survey beyond that line. With tides often of twenty feet this was a lot of survey for the Sappers and it was bravely done under unfriendly conditions starting on D itself. At least this part of the job had started well.

By about 0900 hrs the Germans seemed to disappear and then by one of those kinks that occur in life, an American DUKW with two dead Americans aboard drifted through the Piccadilly Circus of shipping in to HMS *Aristocrat* and the sailors made it fast. Suddenly the penny dropped and the message was taken — here was the unplanned but perfect way to get ashore with dry feet presented out of the skies. My driver, Corporal Antony, a sterling character who had driven lorries before the war, claimed to know how to drive a DUKW, and so with Donald May and Sergeant Major Plenty we set off and arrived on Gold Item beach between Cabane and Asnelles.

Thus, on D-day +1 (7th June) HQ PCF was on station, according to plan. Others, however had already arrived; Lt. Col. R J P Cowan puts all these earliest arrivals in context

The Commander of the entire Mulberry Project, the concrete Caisson breakwater, the piers and pierheads, was a gallant and highly experienced Regular Officer, Brigadier A E M ('Wally') Walter. We found that he was a calm, resolute, charming and kindly man. He must have known what a scratch bunch we were, and that he would never receive the equipment in time to train us, yet knowing all this, he remained, to outward appearance, utterly relaxed and confident.

His Second-in-Command was Colonel A E Howarth, a distinguished and highly respected Engineer in civilian life, with a first class War Record.

Lt. Colonel S K Gilbert was in charge of the construction of the breakwater; I had served under his command in Africa and Italy. I liked and respected him; he was a most able and experienced Engineer, an eccentric in the best tradition of the Corps.

Lt. Colonel A R Mais was responsible for the construction of the piers and the pierheads. He had an enviable reputation, an officer with what the French call 'élan'. He had served with the BEF. in France 1939-40, on the Lofoten Raid, in Northern Persia and with the 8th Army in the Western Desert; he had been posted to Mulberry direct from Combined Operations at Inveraray. He, poor chap, had somehow to get us, the 969th and 970th Companies, ready for the invasion.

His Second-in-Command was Major R J Court, a Civil Engineer in civilian life, keen, hard working, a very nice fellow.

These experienced Officers inspired confidence; they had seen a lot of the War; they knew what they were about.

The 969th and 970th Company Officers (the two Companies were inextricably mixed together and operated as one) were :

Captain Edward Wallace Witcomb — a large, charming, polished, very English, Englishman, born and educated in the USA, a metallurgist, who had come home from Chile to fight with the British Army. He had already seen service in Africa. He was in charge of the Pierhead crews.

Captain A R K Simpson — a tea-taster and a yachtsman in civilian life. Hard driving, efficient, meticulous, he trained the pier construction team.

Captain John Luck had been a tug skipper on the River Thames. Quiet, dependable, capable, skilled. He commanded the tugs and tows.

Captain George Tarling, a stout-hearted regular soldier, a highly competent administrator, appalled by us civilian soldiers, determined that we should not let down his beloved Corps. He had known Witcomb in Africa.

The Junior Officers were keen, fit young men, mostly straight from Officers Training Units — full of energy, ready for anything — Lieutenants A J Hirst, P C Pollard, D W Barton, W W Rigbye, D Jones, G T Budworth. They were going to need all their energy, and guts, in the days ahead.

Their spirits remained high, raised by the knowledge that the waiting and uncertainty was behind them, even though they faced a task never attempted before. Lt. Col. Cowan takes up the story

The Company embarked at Tilbury Dock (on 4th June) on the *City of Canterbury*; John Luck, with Hirst and Budworth sailed with the pontoon bridge sections; Ted Witcomb with Barton and his men were towed away on board the spud pierheads .

Half trained, if that, we were on our way.

It is difficult to describe the atmosphere of those exciting days of high tension. As we set off, Arthur Hirst, a cultured and poetic lad, was heard to quote:-

> And gentlemen of England, now abed,
> Shall think themselves accursed they were not here,
> And hold their manhoods cheap while any speaks,
> That fought with us upon St. Crispin's Day.

He was told to shut up, but we wouldn't have changed places with anyone.

Captain Tarling — a proud Regular soldier and quite appalled by the ill-assorted rabble he was leading on to the battlefield — but determined for the honour of the Corps of Royal Engineers to make us act like soldiers — watched the Company shuffle aboard the *City of Canterbury* and remarked, (he attributed this to Wellington, speaking of his troops before Waterloo): 'I don't know what they will do to the enemy, but, by God, they frighten me'.

Colonel Mais, Bobby Court, and C S M Braysford landed on D-day (6th June 1944) to survey the beaches and to set out the lines of the piers and the shore approaches. After wading ashore through the surf at Le Hamel they found the direct road to Arromanches mined and under fire and set off inland. They had an exciting, hair-raising, time working their way along narrow, leafy lanes, across fields, through scattered units of the German Army, to their destination.

Ted Witcomb arrived off Omaha Beach where his pierhead was peppered with machine gun and small arms fire. He could see that there was a lot of nastiness on the beach and was delighted to be towed quickly away to the quieter shore at Arromanches.

Luck, in his steam tugs, made landfall at the Port-en-Bessin area; he too came under heavy fire from the shore until re-directed by the Royal Navy to Arromanches.

The main body, with Tarling, Simpson, Rigbye and myself, landed on D+1 Day (7th June) at King's Beach (La Rivière); we were taken ashore on an Assault Landing Craft by a happy and very young Canadian Midshipman. It was quiet and trouble free; a few shells fell some 200 yards to the east as we were guided up the beach and through the minefields by very smart and polite Military Policemen.

Someday, when I dandle my grandchildren on my knee and tell them of the Normandy landings, I shall recount a much more thrilling story of shot and shell. A keen cinema-goer, I recall enough of the film 'The Longest Day' to frighten the little stinkers out of their boots.

At the head of the beach, leaning on a gate, I met Jimmy Whitton, a Major in the Artillery; an old school friend from Glasgow who had come ashore on D-day. He offered me tea, asked for my family and then directed our steps towards Arromanches, where we found Brigadier Walter and Colonel Mais sitting on the sea wall, laughing and talking.

Further details of the old Clyde paddle steamer HMS *Aristocrat*, and of her role as transport to Brigadier Walter, the Commander of the whole Mulberry project, are given by Alan Brown and Richard Polglaze, the latter who sailed in her to Normandy. HMS *Aristocrat* was amongst the great crowd of shipping and Mulberry equipment, waiting in the Solent for the order to get under way.

For a while *Aristocrat* tied up alongside HMS *Despatch*, a cruiser which was to be the Headquarters Ship of the Naval and Military Officers in charge of the Mulberry B Harbour construction. We just couldn't understand why we, a relatively unimportant ship, should be in such august company, although, unknown to us at the time, *Aristocrat* had been allocated the role of support ship to the *Despatch*, then stationed in the Lee-on-Solent/Cowes section of the Solent. An order was issued that the ship was now 'closed' and that nobody would be allowed ashore except for officers to receive their final briefings. We neither sent nor received mail and such was the need for secrecy that these orders applied to the entire Solent fleet.

The installation of Mulberry B Harbour came under the Joint Naval and Military Command of Capt. C H Petrie, DSO, RN, (Hydrographer) and Brigadier A E M Walter CBE RE, their unit being entitled 'Headquarters Port Construction Force'. Captain Petrie was in charge of the provision, placing and sinking of the blockships, whilst Brigadier Walter was in charge of the caissons, other sea defences and the construction of the port itself. Both had a considerable number of staff. On Saturday 3 June the main party of the Port Construction Force embarked on *Aristocrat*, with the remainder following the next day. There were now dozens of extra men on board including a Royal Engineers squad for work ashore and a party of Naval Signalmen to direct and control the tugs, blockships and other craft employed in construction work. They had to sleep wherever they could find a spare space, and when a crew member returned from watch he'd usually find someone asleep in his bunk. In total we had 25 officers and 55 men of various ranks quartered on board plus as many stores as could be crammed into the ship. Actually, we all got on very well together in our mess where we had as guests about eight pongos — soldiers who were not REs but a military signals squad who were to work with the REs when they went ashore at Arromanches. We were very fortunate in that one of our guest soldiers had been a baker in Civvy Street and he made us some marvellous fresh bread, something we very seldom got. He also showed us how to make the bread and had quite an audience when demonstrating mixing, rolling and kneading the dough.

Before we left for Arromanches Rear Admiral W G Tennant CB RN, who was in charge of the whole operation came on board to confer with Capt. Petrie and Brigadier Walter. Never had we seen so many high ranking naval and military officers on board *Aristocrat*, but we were still unaware of the important role *Aristocrat* was destined to play in the near future. The invasion fleet was now ready to sail and on 5 June we lined the decks of *Aristocrat* to watch the huge armada weigh anchor, giving the ships and troops a wave as they passed us to line up in groups for crossing the Channel to their respective landing beaches on the Normandy coast. There was a great apprehension as to what sort of reception lay ahead and the atmosphere on board *Aristocrat* was rather subdued that night. The next day, 6 June 1944 (D-day), we went alongside HMS *Despatch* at 10.00 a.m. and realised that *Aristocrat* was herself to cross that day and that initially we were to be the HQ ship at Arromanches. Just before we sailed a party of Official Photographers came aboard, who later took a number of photographs during the crossing and off the beach-head. *Aristocrat*, now bristling with aerials and radio equipment of a most advanced and unusual nature, cast off at 14.30 and as she steamed away from her parent ship the skirl of the pipes suddenly echoed across the still waters of the Solent; on *Aristocrat's* deck Alec. Mitchell, the Electrical Officer, was giving the ship and her companions a rousing send-off in the traditional Scottish manner.

First of all she had to rendezvous with a number of tugs and merchantmen before heading south to cross the Channel by the swept, buoy-marked route to the invasion beaches. A screen of destroyers patrolled each side of the swept fairway and one of these came up on our quarter with a message that had to be passed over manually, which in those days was done by firing a 0.303 rifle with a special bolt and a line attached. The message was then put in a metal container, fastened to the line, and hauled across to its destination, when to our surprise we discovered that one of their gun crew had previously served on board *Aristocrat*. The crew was now on a two watch system, watch and watch, so we spent most of the time closed up at our guns. In addition we had to stand-to at dusk and dawn so there was not much opportunity for sleep; the off-duty watch just crashed down in the mess and everyone remained fully dressed. When dawn broke we lay quite a way off the beach on Gold Sector at Arromanches, and as it was a lovely sunny morning we could see the initial landing force craft (possibly including the second wave too) milling about on the other

sectors to the east and west of us. A number of the larger Infantry
Landing Craft passed us on their way back to the UK to reload and
bring up reinforcements. Off shore were the naval support ships —
battleships, cruisers and rocket firing craft — giving cover to the
troops ashore and knocking out gun emplacements as requested. There
seemed to be continuous air cover over the beaches, the black and white
zebra strips below the wings and on the bodies of the aircraft making
them instantly recognisable and although there was little enemy
activity we nevertheless could clearly hear the sounds of battle inland.

As it got lighter we steamed cautiously forward towards the beach
and at approximately 4.30 a.m. anchored about ¼ mile offshore. To our
surprise there was very little sign of damage or destruction along the
coast in our area and we later learned that the actual assault on Gold
Beach had been made to the east of Arromanches by the Hampshire and
Dorsetshire regiments, who encircled the town and then took it from
the rear. The plan, of course, was to keep the beaches in what was to be
the Mulberry 'B' Harbour undamaged and accessible from both land
and sea. We were the first Port Construction Force ship to arrive at
Arromanches, in fact, I don't recollect any other ships being there
before us. The first craft to come alongside was a small Survey motor
launch carrying the officers who had placed buoys to mark the
positions where the blockships were to be sunk, thereby forming a
breakwater protection for the harbour proper. Next alongside was one
of the two USA tugs which had crossed with us and up the bridge
ladder came the captain who thrust out his hand to Captain Petrie and
said 'I'm Tony Martin'. Now to address an RN Captain in this manner
was unheard of, but Captain Petrie merely introduced himself in a
similar informal manner and then got down to instructing the tug
captain what jobs he wanted the tugs to do. Shortly afterwards the tug
brought alongside a DUKW with two dead US soldiers aboard which
had drifted down from the American Sector, about 12 miles to the west
of Gold. The Americans on Omaha Beach had been pinned down and
lost a lot of men so other bodies and military equipment kept floating
past us eastwards. The DUKW was requisitioned by Brigadier Walter,
who then took his first trip ashore to try and find a suitable HQ. By
now the first blockships had arrived and Brigadier Walter returned to
Aristocrat for the big event of the day, the sinking of the first of these,
the *Alynbank*, at 13.50 on D+l.

Unfortunately, due to some of the tugs having gone astray and the
need to keep to the strict timetable, *Alynbank* was sunk without their
assistance and in the process slewed badly out of line. However, tugs
arrived in time for the sinking of the second blockship, the *Saltersgate*,
when all went according to plan. As soon as sufficient of the blockships

had been positioned and sunk it was considered safe for us to move and we tied up alongside the *Saltersgate*.

Shortly afterwards we acquired a small landing craft, from where I have no idea, which we needed to use when the telecommunication cable brought across on *Aristocrat* was laid from the *Alynbank* to the signal station ashore. At about this time most of the troops had left *Aristocrat*, some staying aboard the sunken blockships and others finding quarters ashore, though as HQ ship we still had Captain Petrie and Brigadier Walter and some of their staff with us. Insofar as enemy activity was concerned it was conspicuous by its absence and things were very quiet where we were. Shells occasionally fell around us but nothing really interfered with all the intense activity off Arromanches. At night German planes frequently came over but much to our regret we were not allowed to open fire since this could betray our position and the harbour activity. Of course, one night the inevitable happened, a gun opened fire and next thing we were all at it. The bells started to ring and we were ordered to cease fire immediately. Every ship had received a signal on D+1 which read: 'No ship shall open fire with close weapons after dark to safeguard our fighters and prevent giving away the position of the anchorage' and continued 'All commanding officers shall be held personally responsible and there shall be no departure whatsoever from these rules. Should they be broken I shall require the captain to attend the Flagship and give his explanation' signed, Rear Admiral Talbot. No wonder the bells rang. During the early days, at dusk, we used to set off smoke floats and become engulfed in the foul black fug; fortunately the practice was soon discontinued since it was considered more important to be able to observe any mines dropped by enemy aircraft and because it interfered with the unloading of ships and construction of the harbour itself.

On 11 June HMS *Despatch* took over as HQ ship, our hour of glory was over! Captain Petrie and his staff transferred to *Despatch*, Brigadier Walter's party went ashore and we now took up station outside the harbour, where *Aristocrat* reverted to the more mundane duties of convoy routing and anti-aircraft protection. With convoy examination officers now on board, incoming ships were directed to their various beaches or pontoons in order to ensure the smooth and efficient use of the harbour facilities.

Brigadier Walter's account also describes the mis-handling of the scuttling of *Alynbank,* but goes on to show how the Navy profited by this one error of judgement. Late on the morning of D-day, Brigadier Walter, who had been reconnoitring ashore, returned to the beach. He tells how he made contact with Donald May and

. . . went down to the sea front which we had looked at from the sea at dawn. There it was, just as on the model and on the photos we had pored over for long hours in Norfolk House, and unbelievably here we were at last. It was exciting and inspiring and gave a terrific urge to get cracking without delay. After looking around we embarked once more in our DUKW and returned to HMS *Aristocrat* for the first big planned event in the planting of Mulberry B — the scuttling at 1350 hours by the Navy of the blockship (or Corncob) *Alynbank*. Everything went wrong — she settled too slowly and the tugs failed to hold her on line as she sank and she ended up more or less at right angles to the intended line of the breakwater. This was a bad start but the Navy immediately learnt the lesson and in the following days successfully planted their part of the breakwater. The remainder of the harbour breakwaters were formed by the concrete caissons (Phoenix) planted by 930 PC&R Company and the Royal Navy.

After this excitement I went ashore again and did a first complete recce of Arromanches with Raymond Mais and Donald May. Detachments of the PCR had been arriving all day and I met Ronnie Cowan with a party of 969 PFEC and Major Hinrichs with a party of 935 PC&R Company. Already the planning seemed to be falling into place and didn't seem quite so barmy after all. We ended the day by bivouacking in a wood to the west of Arromanches as dusk was falling. We dispersed early next morning but about mid-morning there came sounds of battle from the west of the town. Later it transpired that a party of about sixty Germans had emerged from underground passages below where we had bivouacked the night before and were engaged by such PCF troops as could be mustered who, with the aid of a tank, killed some but took forty-seven prisoners. So ended the capture of Arromanches on D+2 instead of D-day as planned.

By about D+3, the PCF had at long last become a living entity. For the first time all the constituent units were working on one site, each on its own specialised task. To me it all came to life and all ranks soon became imbued with a tremendous spirit to lick all the odds, which became greater as the days went on up to the great storm starting on 19 June. It was an unforgettable and proud experience. The story from inside the PFE Companies has been well told by Ronnie Cowan in a talk which he gave at Imperial College in June 1975 and this record of an outstanding success by RE Units in war should have a place in the *Journal*. Unfortunately no one has recorded the inside story of 930 PC&R Company, some of whose members lost their lives crossing the Channel on the *Phoenix* units under dangerous and very uncomfortable conditions, while others played their parts so successfully in the planting

of the caissons to form the major part of the breakwaters — a company of
which the Corps can be very proud.

HQ PCF was on site, with all its support forces. From the accounts quoted, the
components of Mulberry were arriving and were in process of being assembled.
How had they travelled? Sir Bruce White puts the scene in context.

> The Mulberry forces were given the order to sail to their destination on
> the afternoon of D-day. It was planned that within fourteen days of the
> first soldiers going ashore, the artificial harbours, both British and
> American, would be in place. The Americans, who had no part in the
> construction of the artificial harbours, did not allow themselves enough
> time to train in their use.

Vice Admiral Hickling gives the clearest possible account of the marshalling,
transporting and assembling of the harbours. He begins with the assembly of all the
separate units from the yards where they were produced.

> By March, 1944, the various units of Bombardon, Phoenix, Whale, and
> Corncob (the cover name for the blockships) were nearing completion. It
> was the intention to assemble them on the South coast of England so as to
> reduce as far as possible the tow to the Far Shore. The Navy had viewed
> with growing concern the problems which the towing of these
> monstrosities was likely to involve. The soldiers had said that they would
> probably tow 'like drunken sailors,' to which the sailors wittily replied,
> 'You mean drunken soldiers,' so all were satisfied. In practice the units,
> with certain exceptions, towed remarkably well. It required the services of
> two hundred tugs, mustered from all over the Kingdom and the United
> States for nearly four months, to collect the 600 units from all round the
> British Isles and bring them down to the South coast. This was
> undoubtedly the biggest towing operation ever undertaken, and but for
> the unremitting efforts of the tugs and the Admiralty Towing Section
> under Rear Admiral Brind, combined with a fine Spring, I doubt if we
> should have been ready for D-day. As it was, when the tugs had
> accomplished their task they only had a few days in which to clean their
> boilers, refit their towing gear and be ready for the passage across the
> Channel. This huge movement threw a heavy additional burden on the
> Cs-in-C, especially in the Portsmouth and Nore commands, who already
> had their hands full with the assault forces.
>
> As I told you, Lord Leathers handed over the oldest crocks he had got
> on his list of ships. He was most gracious about it, but we knew all the
> time that he was only too glad to be rid of these museum pieces, some of
> which were fifty years old — he badly wanted the crews in order to man
> the new Liberty ships coming over from the States. It was on D-7 that the
> blockships, with Captain Hill, RN, in command, left Oban. So great was

the need for secrecy at this stage that even the Masters of the ships could not be truthfully briefed. They were told they were going to do an operation in the Bay of Biscay. We had taken the precaution of sending tugs to help them on their way, which was as well, as the Armada, streaking down the West Coast at 3 knots, was often in difficulties: sometimes they towed one another, sometimes the tugs did the towing. However, they all arrived at Poole on D-1, very pleased with themselves they were too, and I think it was a great achievement on the part of our sister Service to get these sixty old gridirons down there on time.

Eventually they sailed at 4 a.m. on D-day, and so anxious were they to make their Gooseberries that they went right through a minefield — fortunately it did not go off. They arrived at their rendezvous and dispersed to their positions where they were sunk. Truly their last hours were also their greatest.

The assembly of the Mulberry units off the south coast of England must have resulted in near gridlock, before this concept had become even a remote possibility on motorways and in cities. Even if it did not reach that dramatic pitch, it must have cost the organisers much mental anguish before the problem was solved. Vice Admiral Hickling does not minimize the difficulty.

The South Coast of England was already filled to overflowing with the assault forces and it was no easy matter to find suitable places to park the Mulberry units. All had to be protected from the south-westerly blows and from attacks by the enemy, both surface and air. Moreover, the Phoenix units had to be sunk on a flat and sandy bottom as no quays or moorings were available. This, of course, meant a big pumping job when it came to refloating them.

In the event the Bombardons under Captain Currey, RN, 115 of them, were parked at Portland, the Blockships at Poole, and the Whale Pier roadway — some eighty-four tows, each 480 ft. long (six 80 ft. sections) — were moored on the Peel Bank near Ryde. The tugs — 150 special Mulberry tugs, were based at Lee-on-Solent and were administered by Captain Moren, US Navy, and a fine job he made of it.

Of the Phoenixes and the Whale pierheads, two-thirds were parked at Selsey and one-third at Dungeness. You may well ask why were these valuable units placed right under the guns of Calais. The answer is that it was part of the Cover Plan. The object of the Cover Plan was to lead the enemy up the garden path or rather up the Pas de Calais to make him think we were going to land in the Narrows. We did everything that we could to mislead him; for instance before D-day for every bomb that was dropped on the Normandy beaches, three were dropped in the Pas de Calais area. In order to soothe the soldiers — who were naturally rather anxious about them — we got a professor to work out the probability of these units at Dungeness being damaged. He reckoned that if the enemy fired 1,000 rounds — all he could do in the time — there would be eleven hits. So the Army was placated. In point of fact they were not fired on at all. The enemy went on firing at Dover, so everyone was happy — except possibly Dover.

The month of May was very hectic, for all the units had to be got ready for the crossing. The pier roadways were put together at Marchwood and Richborough and were then towed to the Peel Bank, and it was during this assembly stage that we realized they were going to give trouble. Erection tanks were a weak spot and some of the tows came to grief while crossing the Solent. No proper provision had been made for mooring the eighty-four Whale tows at Peel Bank but fortunately the Commander-in-Chief, Portsmouth, came to the rescue. The preparation of the units for sea involved a very large amount of boat work taking parties and stores to and from the shore. The British were lamentably short of water transport and appealed to the Americans who helped us out considerably with the loan of DUKWS and small tugs.

There was very nearly a major disaster over the pumping equipment for raising the Phoenixes, eight to ten of which it was intended to raise and send across the Channel daily. Four little Dutch schuyts had been fitted out with a Heath Robinson arrangement of pumps in which none of us had very much confidence. A lucky accident had put one of the Phoenixes aground on the Bramble Bank in Southampton Water, and it had taken a salvage tug a week to get it afloat again. This made us think a bit, and as time went on, and the Dutch schuyts did not materialize, Tennant took drastic action. He took over responsibility for the whole of the pumping out equipment and appealed to the Admiralty, but only just in time. For a month, work under Captain Polland, R.N.V.R., went on night and day, and by mobilizing the whole of the Salvage organization the situation was saved; but it was a near thing.

By the exercise of ingenuity, initiative and sheer determination, the assembly was achieved by the 5th of June, D-1. And, as the November 1944, *Shipyard Spotlight*, was later to boast in 'The Tugs were there too!'

Big Fellows from Leith

Nearly 150 tugs of all sizes helped to get the harbours across the Channel. Among them were big fellows from Robb's and others less big from Cochrane's. They took the blockships, the piers, the bridge-spans, the pierheads and the breakwaters to the two rendezvous on the French coast. When you learn that the new harbours were comparable in size with Dover or Gibraltar, you have some idea of the gigantic tows involved.

Allies Represented

Thirty-three H.M. tugs and 43 tugs from the Merchant Navy formed the
bulk of the towing force, and they were assisted by several Dutch,
Belgian and French vessels. On the other side, 31 large American tugs
and 36 smaller ones helped to place the main units in position. For the
final jockeying, British 'tids' (short for 'tiddlers'), small prefabricated tugs
built by Dunstan's, were used. They were manned by British and
American crews.

All this great flotilla of tugs were under the command of Captain John Luck
who, before the war had skippered a Thames tug. Now he was in charge of over
145 tugs of all sizes, of different power and speed capacity, facing a towing
challenge greater than any ever previously attempted, in the notoriously
unstable sea conditions of the Channel, and under the threat of enemy attack
by air, sea or minefield. The responsibility placed on him was unbelievably
heavy.

Vice Admiral Hickling takes up the tale of the crossing.

By superhuman efforts the Assembly was completed and the units made
ready for sea just about the time the assault forces were leaving harbour
on D-1. The first Mulberry left harbour in the evening of D-day. For
purposes of planning we had worked out an integrated towing
programme, because each unit had to be moved into the harbour in its
proper place and proper order at the proper time. Of course we realized
that with so many unknown factors, including enemy action, our
programme could never be strictly adhered to, but it provided a very good
guide. In our planning we had allowed a towing speed of three knots —
actually an average speed of four knots was achieved. We allowed one
day in four when bad weather would prevent towing — unfavourable
weather prevailed most of the time. We allowed for the loss of fifteen tugs,
but only two went to the bottom. We allowed for a 20 per cent loss of the
units to be towed — our losses of Bombardons, Phoenixes and Pierheads
were negligible; our loss of Pier Roadways, due to bad weather, was of
the order of 50 per cent.

Each night, depending on the weather forecast, the following units
were despatched to each Mulberry

4 to 5 Phoenixes
6 Bombardons.
2 or 3 Pierheads.
4 or 5 sections of Pier Roadways.

It was so arranged that they should not enter the combat area
during dark hours owing to the presence of enemy E-boats. When the
units arrived on the far side they were taken over by harbour tugs so
that the sea-going tugs could return for another tow. The Whale units

would then be turned over to the Sappers, while the Planter,
Lieutenant-Commander Lampen, RN, and his team, would board the
Phoenix and, if conditions served, plant it. It was quite remarkable with
what accuracy the Phoenix breakwater was placed, often under
difficult conditions of wind, tide and light.

The work of building the harbour went reasonably well for the first
few days, the Gooseberries being finished on D+5 to what Admiral Vian
described as 'the great satisfaction of all'. By D+8, the Bombardon had
been finished and was giving very good results with a wave suppression
of about 40 per cent. By D+10 the Mulberry breakwaters were about half
completed and the Whale Piers about one-third. The Americans at
Mulberry A were building somewhat faster than we were at Mulberry B,
but my impression when I was over there on D+5 was that they were not
taking so much care. I did not think the blockships were locked close
enough in together and I reported to Admiral Tennant that some of the
Phoenixes had been planted in too deep water. Some of them even at
Neap tides had barely a foot freeboard at high water. The trouble with the
Phoenix was that the units were weak to internal pressure, not as might
be expected, to external attack by the sea. They would fill up with water
and then, due to the difference of hydraulic head inside and out, would
burst. This structural defect was overcome by fitting roofs. The latest
type, the Ax, stood up well.

Being present on a Phoenix under tow was not something to be taken lightly. There
was a constant threat of enemy attacks, some of which were succesful. Robert
Pintar of the 97th–108th Seabees battalion tells his story:

> The 97th & 108th Seabees were on the Isle of Wight the morning of June 6th
> D-day.
>
> June 5th: The sky was full of planes as far as you could see and it was
> deafening. My seabags were all packed.
> June 6th: We did some target shooting into the English Channel. After
> lunch we got ready to go to War.
> June 7th: Got dressed with five layers of clothing plus a rubber tube
> life jacket. Stopped to eat lunch. We were given six pork chops and a loaf
> of bread. This was to be our dinner. Went on board our Phoenix base,
> 200 ft x 60 ft. x 60 ft. about 1300 hrs. We had six British soldiers who
> were to man our 40 mm anti-aircraft gun, they were in the bow quarters.
> We were in the stern quarters. We left our river dockage early afternoon
> by a USA tugboat towing us at 4 knots per hour headed for Omaha beach
> to arrive at dawn on June 8th. The six of us Seabees were paired off to
> stand 4 hour watch each.
> June 8th: I went on watch at 24 hrs.with Chief Isaac Willingham. We
> were to be the second caisson to arrive by dawn. It was dark: the skies

were full of planes, ships all around, red skies on the coast of France, sounds of War gave chills up the spine! Standing on the stern deck and watching the tug boat towing us at 01.15 hrs I heard a splash splash and a hissing sound on the port side and saw two torpedoes skimming along the surface that crossed our bow and aft of the tug boat — missed us! The Germans misjudged our slow speed of 4 knots, the tug cut us loose! I was speechless, then hollered below to the four Seabees, 'Torpedoes - Torpedoes' (May-Day all on deck), then ran along the gangway to the bow quarters to alert the soldiers with the same warning. I ran back to the stern and made sure Chief Willingham's Mae West was tied on tight. At this time we could hear the deep throated diesel sound of the enemy E-Boat and two more torpedoes splashing as they were launched. We watched them hissing along the surface in a foam of death towards us. One along our starboard and the other along our port side, both from the stern. Both missed again. By this time I had cut our one life raft loose. (How dare the Germans shoot at us.) We were all on deck now; looking, and listening; looking and listening. Harry Winslow and myself were standing on the stern. Off in a distance, dead center of our stern, we heard the 'splash - splash'; one torpedo was off to starboard. Harry and I leaned over the stern rail to watch. The torpedo slammed into our stern with an almighty 'KA-BOOM'. We were about 45 ft. above water. We were blown about 20 ft. into the air, by the time we landed back on the concrete deck, the caisson was listing to port at 30 degrees and sinking fast. We slid and tumbled on the deck to port and into the cold sea. The sinking caisson sucked us down with it to the bottom of the English Channel, about 25 fathoms depth, ten miles from France. The noises under water seemed to me to be made by angels hollering, plus the sound of underwater explosions and many air bubbles.

When we came up to surface Winslow and I found the life raft along with three others to float on. Chief Willingham found a case of 'K' rations to float on. All five of these mates were strangers to me and just put together as a crew a few weeks earlier. We were all fighting to keep alive. We still heard the sound of the enemy's diesel as he patrolled around us. Chief Willingham was crying out 'God save us' very loud, and out of the darkness came the German E-Boat. We could see the skullcap bridge. A machine gunner opened fire and laced the water in front of Chief Willingham and fired from bottom to top. Chief Willingham was gone! The E-Boat disappeared into the darkness.

All through the night's early hours, we would be silent or whisper. Winslow and I would take turns to hold up two soldiers who did not have any life-jackets on — we didn't see any life in them, as time passed we were numb and cold and let them slip under! During the time in the water we were drifting towards Cherbourg and Omaha. We encountered many body parts and dead bodies, like 'fishing bobbers', heads down, feet up, drowned. The sea was full of debris. 'What a solemn sight'. Harry Winslow lost his hearing, one got his leg crushed. All the others were also banged up. We watched the red glow at night along with the sounds of explosions.

June 8th: 0635 hrs: The coming of dawn, we sighted to the west a ship, it came closer it was HMS *Vivacious*, a light destroyer. It stopped to pick us up putting its starboard bow alongside. The crew put its cargo nets overside. Just then the HMS *Vivacious* crew pointed to the eastern sky. We looked up just in time to see a German Stuka J-87-D nose over, with its wing dive brakes in position, along with its 110 lbs bombs slung under its belly, its two dive sirens screeching.

The crew of HMS *Vivacious* along with us survivors were motionless as we awaited the bombs! Two loud KA-BOOMS. We were about 20 ft. from the starboard side of the ship as the bombs landed in the water between the ship and us. The concussion blew our legs back up under the wood frame of the life raft. The back of my legs were all shredded. The Stuka came out of its dive and disappeared into the clouds. The crew of HMS *Vivacious* had to help us up the cargo nets. We were numb and cold. We would not have lasted long. The crew helped remove our clothes, wrapped us in blankets and gave us a grog of rum and hot tea. The crew dried our oil[ed] and shredded clothes and gave them back to us to wear. The British officer of HMS *Vivacious* notified us that we were now Prisoners of War.

June 9th: We were turned over to the British War Ministry [who treated our wounds] and interrogated each of us. We were taken to London and put up in a hotel on the second floor near Piccadilly Circus; how convenient! Early that evening we climbed out of the window, down the fire escape and off to Piccadilly Circus. In oily-shredded invasion clothes only with French Invasion money. We went into a pub. Didn't need money! Soon, 'Scotland Yard Dicks' were with us; they escorted us back to the hotel. Same guard at the door and another guard at outside window.

Robert Pintar was awarded the first of two Purple Heart medals as a result of the wound he gained in the English Channel.

Until Monday 19th June, the weather was good. Captain Luck's luck held: the tows were going according to plan, (except for the Pier roadway, the most intractable load of all) some of which had been held up by doubtful forecasts. It was hoped that, during the next few days, even this could be brought back into schedule. It was however, an unfounded hope. Against all the odds, Mulberry had been planted. Now it was nearly to be uprooted by the forces of nature. For all those who had laboured so hard and for so long, it must have been a bitter experience, probably best expressed, many years later, by Major General Sir Donald J McMullen, Director of Transportation. During a meal with his family one day, he firmly announced: 'We are *never* going to grow a Mulberry bush.'

Not only did the transportation of the Mulberries pose a problem, so too did transporting the forces which used the harbours. Some were taken to France in passenger and merchant ships; some went in specially designed vessels (LCTs and LCMs); but an Army needs copious supplies, and material for repair of equipment and that also must be shipped. It is unexpected, to say the least, to find that Thames lighters were used to ship supplies. Lt. W D (Jim) Jarman gives a useful account of what they did.

> In the build-up of men and material for 'Operation Overlord' it was becoming increasingly apparent that there was a serious shortage of seaborne support for the British and American assault forces, which was now to cover three British and two American beachheads. Admiral Lord Louis Mountbatten, when Chief of Combined Operations, had requisitioned a thousand Thames lighters of which four hundred were converted for the Royal Navy. These lighters were engineless flat-bottomed barges serving the London River by lightermen using wooden sweeps. Their conversion did not produce a very seaworthy vessel. The idea of crossing the Channel in any sort of sea state, other than flat calm, had the makings of a nightmare. For many of the men, that is exactly what it was. The role of the Landing Barges was to support the British and American armies assaulting the five beachheads by providing repair facilities, the provision of diesel, petrol, water and food to all craft. In addition, some barges were converted to carry Bofors gun manned by men of the Royal Artillery to assist with the protection of the artificial harbour in the British sector. Others carried a variety of jerricans of fuel and ammunition and were aptly described as floating bombs; they also assisted with the off-loading of stores from coasters for which they were well versed. The majority of the coxswains were lightermen from the London and Humber rivers.
>
> I joined Landing Barges, and undertook a variety of training, including Exercise Jantzen at Tenby, when a number of us sank one night when fully laden during gale force winds. Captain Harrison Wallace, who was in overall command of the Barges confirmed that an artificial harbour was essential!
>
> I was transferred to ferry duties collecting converted barges from the upper reaches of the Thames and congregating at Queenborough until a sufficient number of us were ready to take them, during the night, through the Straits of Dover, (known as 'hellfire corner') onward to Portsmouth. The coxswains being Thames lightermen were fantastic.

129

I returned to Landing Barges and took command of LBE49 (Landing Barge Engineering), of the 36th Supply & Repair Flotilla, at Southampton. More training now; with a permanent crew of over twenty men, we eventually received our briefing to go to GOLD (King sector green) BEACH, which was immediately north of Mont Fleury where the Germans had a battery of four 150 mm guns! D-day was Monday 5th June. We were to proceed to Chichester harbour and await instructions. We moored off Itchenor. D-day was postponed twenty-four hours and confirmed for Tuesday 6th June. The weather was windy and overcast. General Rommel was advised that this was not invasion weather and went to see his wife for her birthday.

At around 2130 on the 5th June, there was an increasing surge of engine noise as a multitude of barges and other landing craft turned on their engines. The white ensigns were flowing freely from the stern of all craft. It was all quite a sight. The crews waved to each other and shouted encouraging comments as we let go our buoys or hauled in the anchors.

We were soon outside the harbour where we were met with a confrontation of wind and tide. The barge soon took up her familiar wallowing gait. Wind and spray flew in our faces, and it was dark, with larger and faster craft overhauling us.

By mid-day to early afternoon we arrived at a beachhead with a warship slowly cruising between the shore and us, pumping shells into the distance. The captain advised us to proceed further west, which we proceeded to do. It was very noisy with numerous craft coming and going with various states of damage. We were soon in business quickly, taking in tow LCMs for repair and casting them off as we proceeded to our allotted anchorage. The 'debris' of war was apparent all round us with bodies floating, and steering the barge, it was better to cast a blind eye and forge ahead.

A number of barges failed to arrive, with crews having no known burial place. Others were buried in cemeteries in north Normandy.

The great gale [19th June] played havoc with all ships and craft and the vital unloading of supplies was severely hampered. The part placed by Landing Barges has been well recorded and their presence was short as the armies gained ground along the coastline through to Holland.

Nobody knew, when the invasion of Europe was planned, how far the Armed Forces might achieve command of the air. Walter King Webster (formerly RNVR) explains how the invasion fleet tried to protect itself from air attack, and gives a lively account of what that Fleet was made of.

I was serving in the Kites and Balloon section of the Directorate of Miscellaneous Weapons Development. It had been decided that if a potentially dangerous wire was suspended vertically above a ship, it was at least off-putting to an enemy dive bomber, or other low-flying aerial attacker, and, hopefully, lethal.

Kites had proved unpractical, but small, rather elegant balloons, some 30 to 40 feet long, were being used to protect mainly merchant ships. Their gear consisted of a hand-winch on deck, on which the wire was wound, and a flying off block (FOB) clamped to the masthead, up to and through which the wire was led.

Immediately below the balloon was a sealed canister in which was packed a 4 ft. parachute beautifully made of the best Egyptian cotton, and also a clever little device which cut the wire cable if an aircraft struck the wire below it.

At the FOB there was a similar parachute and cutting device. If, therefore, an aircraft struck the wire, the wire was severed below the balloon and above the masthead, and the aircraft departed towing the two parachutes. If they didn't tip it into the sea immediately, the drag of the parachutes was sufficient to ensure that it ran out of fuel before it reached home.

The RAF was responsible for inflating and servicing the balloons, which were then passed to the Navy, which in turn took them out to the ships, and brought back those which were beginning to sag. My job, as a kite and balloon officer (KBO), had been to check the winches and FOBs on merchant ships in Hull docks, assisted by three sailors.

At the approach of D-day, I was transferred to a naval balloon unit, based at Flathouse Quay in Portsmouth Harbour. There were some half-dozen of us KBOs there, and a team of ratings. Our duty was to take balloons to and from the invasion vessels.

I spent a lot of my time afloat in the anchorages in the lee of the Isle of Wight. There, the invasion fleet lay at anchor. Largest were the commandeered peacetime passenger vessels, and other merchant ships in one of which Barbara[15] made her crossing. After them came the LSTs (Landing Ships Tank). These were proper seagoing craft of several hundred tons, with extremely shallow draught, and a lowering ramp forward for loading and beaching their cargo of vehicles.

Then came the LCTs (Landing Craft Tank). These were little more than large, shallow boxes. They had been welded together in any engineering works with welding equipment, and were only expected to last one or two crossings to France. Forward, they had a lowering ramp and aft was the machinery, the bridge and basic accommodation for their own crews and those of the vehicles carried. However, they were much subdivided, so as to be unsinkable unless very severely damaged. Tales were told of LCTs, which had broken in two at sea, returning under their

---

[15] Barbara's account follows on page 158.

131

own power, with the after -half towing the forward one, but these may well be apocryphal.

Many LCTs were manned by a fascinating collection of piratical desperadoes, who realised that life might well be short, and ought therefore to be lived to the full.

In order to get to and from the invasion fleet with our balloons, we had at our disposal an interesting assemblage of small craft. Perhaps the most intriguing and picturesque were a steam pinnace and a steam picket boat. These were designed to be carried on the side decks of pre-1914 coal-fired battleships. Some 60 or more feet long, they were very narrow, with a foc'sle forward, a saloon aft, and powerful coal-fired steam machinery amidships. When flat-out under forced draught, a yard or so of flame arose from their bell-topped funnels, and they stormed along like miniature destroyers.

Apart from them we had traditional steam powered harbour launches, and a variety of peacetime fishing craft and yachts.

I can't remember much of most of my fellow KBOs. Our CO was a likeable and efficient Lt. Knight, but all I can remember was his bewailing the fact that he liked gin, whereas all he had access to was rather watery beer.

However Lt. C D Sweet was indeed unforgettable. A peacetime schoolmaster who taught engineering, he was the most amiable of men. As one of our number said, 'Sweet by name and sweet by nature'. He somehow got hold of a sizeable motor yacht, in the deck saloon of which he presided at mealtimes with himself at the head of the table, a Chief Petty Officer at the foot, and the junior ratings down either side. It *was*, of course, highly irregular, but it worked admirably, so no one objected.

So we have at last seen Mulberry, and the troops whom it was to serve so well, crossing the Channel to the coast of Normandy. Everybody involved in that invasion recognised that they were doing something unprecedented in European history, and were proud to be part of it. But for two men, participation was not possible; and it is both sad and, at the same time, delightful, to contemplate their dilemma. The following letter from HM King George VI explains it all.

Buckingham Palace

31ˢᵗ May 1944

My dear Winston,

I have been thinking a great deal of our conversation yesterday and I have come to the conclusion that it would not be right for either you or I to be where we planned to be on D-day. I don't think I need to emphasise what it would mean to me personally or to the whole Allied cause, if at this juncture a chance bomb, torpedo or even a mine should remove you from the scene; equally a change of Sovereign at this moment would be a serious matter for the country and Empire. We should both I know love to be there, but in all seriousness I would ask you to reconsider your plan.

THE STORM

Our story opened with Vice Admiral Hickling's remark that the invasion was threatened by two enemies, the Germans and the weather. He feared the second more than the first; and the accuracy of his judgement was borne out by the event.

Despite the initial delay, again the result of doubtful weather, and some losses, the result both of enemy action and of unavoidable accident, the invasion seemed to have got off to an excellent start. Both British and American Harbours were being rapidly assembled, and brought into service. There were some differences of opinion among the personnel who were responsible, but relations between the Allies remained excellent, as Brigadier Walter relates:

> Sometime in May I had met Captain A D Clark USN who was my opposite number in command of the American Force 128 which was to plant the American Mulberry A at Omaha beach. Their job was to be done entirely by the Navy which included in its organisation Construction Battalion Regiments (CB — known as Seabees) formed from their Naval Corps of Civil Engineers — excellent units composed of engineering trades for marine work which they had developed for their island hopping battles in the Pacific. As the Royal Navy had nothing like this, we British had to bring in the Army and even then the Army had to improvise with specialist marine-engineering units RE, such as the PFE and PC&R Companies. This meant that both the Army and Navy were involved in planting Mulberry B and that our success was dependent on complete unity and co-operation all down the line between two Services, a risk the Americans did not have to take.
>
> Both Clark and I had much the same tight planting schedules to contend with and inevitably in the course of our discussions a friendly rivalry grew up as to which of us would get there first. I explained to him that the Royal Engineers had never been beaten and never would be and so quite obviously we should build faster and better than the Seabees and get a higher tonnage of stores and vehicles ashore quicker than they would! We had a bet on it but for reasons explained below it was never settled.

The 'reasons' were, of course, the great storm of Monday 19th June, of which Vice Admiral Hickling gives a characteristically controlled account.

> It was about D+11 that, as usual, I went along to the Meteorological Office to get the weather forecast which determined what should be sent over that night, and for once the weather prophets, who as you know are a gloomy set of individuals, were all smiles. (It may interest you to know that we sent warships out into the Atlantic for the sole purpose of signalling meteorological reports.) For once there was a really good

weather forecast: for 48 hours it was going to be fine, not a breath of wind, not a ripple on the water. This was just what we had been waiting for. Not only would we get across the daily ration of units but all the back log, all the accumulation of Pier roadway which had been held up by indifferent weather. Altogether we sent over 22 tows of roadway — just above 2½ miles in all. It arrived on the other side, but was sunk in sight of the harbour by the storm.

About 3.30 on Monday, 19th June (D plus 13) it started to blow and it blew for three days and three nights — such a summer gale from the North as had not been known for eighty years: it was a gale which was comparable only to that which in 1588 dispersed the Spanish Armada, and had we not had the Gooseberries and the half-completed Mulberries, I think the Allied armada would have shared the same fate as the Spanish. It is a solemn thought that so much hung on that slender thread.

The gale destroyed the American harbour Mulberry A almost completely. As Cherbourg was likely to fall it was decided not to repair it, although the Gooseberry part of it continued to do good work right up to the time we packed up in Normandy at the end of 1944.

At Mulberry B a certain amount of damage was done. Of course we had the protection of the Calvados Shoal, but that was by no means the only reason why the British harbour survived.

Nevertheless the harbour began to take shape. We were working up to an average discharge of about 9,000 tons a day: 2,000 tons more than the harbour was designed for.

In the days before the storm Lt. Col. Cowan and his men were making a sustained and determined effort to get Mulberry B into working order as soon as possible. Their cheerful but stressful progress ended suddenly, though even in the terrible conditions of the storm, their sense of humour remained unshaken

On 18th June Colonel Mais called an urgent conference. He told us that he feared that the weather was about to deteriorate. He did not know how badly, but no chances would be taken. All moorings must be checked and duplicated; the spud pierheads must be 'spudded up' as far as Ted Witcomb dared. Johnny Luck and John Heming were instructed to get their craft provisioned and fuelled up.

All craft anchored to windward must up-anchor and move out lest they drag anchor and bear down on the piers and pierheads.

Bobbie Court, Joe Beckett and Pollard climbed aboard every ship in the harbour and warned 'up anchor at once or else'. The 'or else' were the Oerlikon guns on the pierheads, manned and ready. A few practice rounds over-head rammed home the message.

Every man was given a hot meal, and we stood by for the worst.

Colonel Mais told me the price of failure to carry out these instructions: my head on a bayonet at the pier end.

Fellow countrymen of mine will recall that the Scottish patriot, Sir William Wallace of Elderslie, was betrayed and captured by the English (about 1300 AD). He was executed at Smithfield in London and his head placed on a pike and exhibited at the Tower of London.

Gentlemen — the lesson from this is that, over the centuries, the English have changed very little.

Raymond Mais was right : on 19th June (D+13) a storm began 'such as had not been seen in the Channel for 80 years — second only to the one that smashed the Spanish Armada in 1588' (Chapter XII *Story of the Mulberries*.[16])

It continued for 4 days — 4 days which no one who served at Arromanches will ever forget. Tired out when it started, the men were far beyond exhaustion point when it finished.

The 969th Company War Diary reads:-

> 19th June. Very stormy weather. Had to fight for the East bridge all day long. US Army towing launches of 334 Harbour Craft Company, and our T.I.D. tugs, do excellent work in towing off craft out-of-control and bearing down on the bridge.

> 20th June. Still stormy. Parties on bridges day and night tightening moorings and fighting to save the structure. US Army launches and our tugs do good work.

> 21st June. Still stormy. Three pierheads damaged, spud legs broken. Tank pier smashed. Men exhausted.

Hardly deathless prose by George Tarling. What he meant to say was that the wind screamed like a banshee, that waves 8 ft. high crashed against the shuddering pierheads and washed over the pontoon bridges making them buck and rear like wild horses, so that the men had to cling to the steelwork or be washed away to drown — and this went on and on, hour after hour, day and night. In the wild daylight and in the dark, out of the gloom would appear crewless, drifting vessels — pursued always by John Luck and John Heming with their British and American tug crews. In the darkness men had to jump from the tugs and from the piers on to these abandoned craft, to attach tow lines so that they could be hauled away. There were some incredible (and unsung) feats of seamanship and daring by Luck and Heming and their men. The Schermuly rocket pistols, for firing light lines, were absolutely invaluable at this time.

---

[16] Hickling, H and Mackillop, I. *Story of the Mulberries*. War Office (1945)

On the piers Simpson and the exhausted but stout-hearted and utterly determined Hirst, Rigbye, Barton, Jones and Budworth, with Sergeants Allen, Westcott, Neale, McMeaken etc., fought like demons with sinking pontoons, dragging anchors and floating equipment which had evaded the tugs. And in the middle of it all, the 'Arromanches Goons', those 'hard men' we had acquired against our will, were splendid and played their part.

Everyone was involved, George Tarling and his office staff, the cooks. Even Doc Smith was heard to say that the only place he could hold the Sick Parade was on the bridges; but he wasn't above lending a hand himself. He watched the frantic efforts to save the pierheads and bridge spans, shaking his head in wonderment and, (he admitted) with reluctant admiration.

The crisis came in the late afternoon of the third day of the storm, just as darkness was falling.

A steel pontoon, blown in by the wind and strong tidal currents, had become lodged underneath one of the bridge spans. With each wave it crashed against the steel trusses and was smashing the end of a concrete 'beetle'. Bill Rigbye, Denny Barton, Sergeant Allen and Sapper Edwards had somehow managed to leap on to the wet and greasy steel deck of the heaving pontoon. Rigbye had hurt his ankle and, unable to move, clung there with the waves breaking over him. As the wind and seas drove the pontoon ever further beneath the bridge girders the position was becoming desperate. It was only a matter of minutes before Rigbye was smashed and crushed.

As I arrived with Doc Smith we found Raymond Mais and Arthur Hirst balanced on the steelwork trying to judge the moment to jump on to the pontoon.

In broad daylight, in dry weather, these leaps would have been extremely hazardous; in the half light, for exhausted men, their reactions slowed by fatigue, it required a special sort of courage. But they succeeded, somehow a line was passed to Luck and Heming, who had edged the sterns of their tugs as close as they dared, and the pontoon was towed away. A wet and cursing Rigbye was rescued and the bridge was saved.

Watching it all, Doc Smith was heard to say, 'What a crowd of mad bloody idiots' and grudgingly as he turned away, 'but brave bloody idiots'.

This was probably the turning point ; nothing changed; darkness fell; the storm continued; but I think we all felt that, from then on, nothing could beat us. And Budworth was heard to say to Jones, 'What price the bloody Goons now?'

On the pierheads Ted Witcomb had 'spudded up' (far beyond the makers' wildest nightmare) so that the warning lights on the control panel were permanently on 'Red', and the warning buzzers shrieked day and night. No place for the faint hearted. In spite of all he could do, spud legs failed and dragged on the bottom. But Witcomb's courage never failed, he kept his nerve, and rode out the storm.

During the night of the third day Brigadier Walter, Colonel Mais and George Tarling decided to visit the spud pontoons to see Witcomb. After a frightening walk along the mile of heaving and undulating bridges, holding grimly on as the waves broke over them, they arrived. The pierheads were awash, shuddering; the noise of the wind, the screech of the spuds grinding on the rocky sea bed, the banging and crashing of the spud legs in the 'guides', was indescribable, frightening.

In the grey dawn they eventually found Ted Witcomb and Jones with a party of men working at makeshift repairs. They were soaked, unshaven, exhausted. The skin below Witcomb's eyes had fallen away: only the spirit of the man was keeping him going. Wally Walter (now himself so tired that he repeated every order twice, just to be sure that he had given it) at once told Tarling to go back for a rum ration as fast as he could — and poor George (in not much better shape than Ted) set off back along the pontoon bridge towards the shore.

The Brigadier and Raymond Mais were desperately concerned about Witcomb and his men, any of whom could have sleep-walked over the side at any time.

Witcomb, courteous and articulate as always, thanked them for visiting him, offered cans of self-heating chocolate (he and his crew lived on these cans during the storms: I wonder if they are still manufactured?). Asked if he could hold on, Ted replied that he could (it was obvious that he would never give in), but said that 'Things were never so bad that they couldn't get worse' and he was right, for almost at once there was an appalling crash. As a tank landing craft (a steel landing ship which carried one tank) crewless, the front door hanging open, had been blown against the pierhead and, with the action of the waves, was smashing itself to bits — and the pierhead deck as well.

Then, out of the grey half-light, rearing and plunging on the waves, came Johnny Luck, Pollard and Heming in the towing launches.

Witcomb and his men managed to attach a tow-line and, with their rocket pistols, they got the line to the tugs. As the wrecked vessel was slowly towed away, Heming came as close alongside as he dared.

Throughout the entire operation, but particularly so during the storm, 'Wally' Walter and Raymond Mais were always among us. They never interfered but were always at our side, helping, encouraging, inspiring us to hold on, willing us not to give in. Remarkably alike in many ways, they both had a great sense of humour, of absurdity, of phrasing their remarks, which never deserted them however tired they were. At the height of the storm Raymond Mais had to call the Junior Officers, now almost totally exhausted with physical effort and over 40 hours without sleep, back to the bridges to deal with some new crisis. When he had disappeared into the howling night Barton was heard to wail in despair — 'It's bloody impossible, we can't do it. . . . if only the bastard didn't make me laugh ,' and off they went to repair the bridges.

Lessons from the Storm:

1. High technical skill, well designed equipment, is essential, but in the end success or failure depends on the courage and determination of the men who use the equipment.

2. Never, ever, give in.

3. Leadership is an art. It is not a matter of shouting orders; you must acquire the liking and the respect of the men, of your employees.

I recall George Tarling's words that, in the Corps, you could always tell a real gentleman — they were the fellows who continued to be courteous even when tired. Wally Walter and Raymond Mais were polite at all times, even when they were exhausted. Remarkable, resolute, brave men, we liked them immensely.

On 23rd June the storm abated, the weather improved, and we started to assess the extent of the damage and destruction. It was an appalling and hopeless scene: corpses, smashed equipment, stores, strewn over the beaches everywhere.

To quote from the *History of the Corps* (of Royal Engineers):

> *The Allied beaches were a sorry and disheartening sight. Hundreds almost thousands, of craft and small ships — some up to 1000 tons deadweight — were lying on the beaches at and above high water mark in a shambles which had to be seen to be believed; craft were actually piled on top of each other two and three deep. But 4 days after the storm the daily overall discharge had risen to 40,000 tons; throughout the storm the Port Operating Sappers somehow managed to off- load the desperately needed stores and ammunition and even on the worst day managed to land 800 tons over the piers.*

It is of interest that over 7000 tons of stores were discharged through the port during the 4 days of storm.

It was Vice Admiral Hickling's boast that, after the storm had passed, the harbour was discharging, on average, about 2000 tons a day of supplies above the capacity for which it had been designed. Cowan's statement that, on average, over 1750 tons per diem had been discharged during the four days of the storm, is even more astonishing.

140

Once the storm had ended, the task of clearing the debris and carrying out repairs proved enormous. Cowan takes up the account.

> On the day after the storm, at first light, Colonel Mais inspected the damage. As he walked along the piers and pierheads the tired, unshaven men greeted him; to every man he gave a salute the Brigade of Guards would have approved. He said nothing, but it was, somehow, a triumphant tour, and we all understood what he meant and what he felt.
>
> The margin between success and complete disaster had, however, been very small: indeed, it had been 'a close run thing'.
>
> As to Mulberry, the centre and east piers had been badly damaged but a scheme for repair and replacement was worked out. Two or three pierheads had broken or bent spuds, which would have to be replaced. But the tank-landing pier was a twisted, hopeless wreck. The pontoon bridge had been turned right over and landing craft etc. were wedged under the smashed pontoons.
>
> The American Mulberry to the west, in a much more exposed situation, had been worse hit than ours by the storm and a decision was made to let the British Mulberry have any equipment — bridge sections, pierheads etc., which had survived there. This enabled us to replace our damaged pierheads and the patched-up concrete beetle pontoons at once; we were greatly encouraged by the unselfish attitude of Colonel Harry E. Bronson (he came from St. Paul, Minnesota) and his Seabee Battalion, from the American Mulberry, during this period; they must have been bitterly disappointed but, great hearted, they did everything they could to help us. Colonel Bronson (a great friend of Raymond Mais) could not have done more for us, and we were very grateful to him and to his men.
>
> Bill Rigbye was given the task of repairing the tank pier. Still in pain from his twisted ankle, he could not walk unaided and had fashioned crutches from two brooms; hardly a military figure as he hobbled along.
>
> I recall standing on top of the cliff above the LST pier with Raymond Mais looking down at the tangled mess, and agreeing that poor Rigbye had been given an almost hopeless job.
>
> We observed two figures among the wreckage — talking and gesticulating; it was Rigbye (easily recognisable with his crutches) and Captain A J Harris (now Professor Harris). I do not know what Harris was doing there (his Company was stationed some distance away in the Beachhead) but, as he eventually became a Consulting Engineer, it is a fair guess that he was giving Rigbye some unwanted advice. Harris had a lot of soldiering ahead of him — in France, Belgium, Holland before he crossed the Rhine into Germany. Raymond Mais took a deep breath.
>
> 'Rigbye', he called 'what are you doing? Get on with it,' and in an undertone, 'The poor fellow, it's impossible'.

Rigbye looked up, beamed and waved a crutch, a small but confident figure.

Aided by Jones he collected bulldozers, heavy cranes, welding and burning gear which he had borrowed from Colonel Bronson at Mulberry A. He acquired all the welders and steel erectors (Sergeants Allen, Westcott, Swayden etc.) and got to work, day and night. He and his men ate and slept on the steelwork: one night Bill Rigbye was found, fast asleep, with a large oxygen cylinder clasped to his bosom, like a bride.

It was astonishing to watch the pier 'come alive' with the odd figure on crutches hobbling around; Sergeants Allen and McMeakin, Sapper Chapman and others working like demons.

In the dark the crippled Rigbye, not surprisingly, fell into the sea; immediately hauled out, spluttering and coughing, he heard Corporal Barnicoat saying 'Poor little bastard, he must be frozen cold' and Sapper Edwards — 'Nonsense he has his greatcoat on'.

In four days — and nights — the pier was repaired and in business; a magnificent achievement.

As Lt.Col. Cowan himself summed it up, 'nothing is impossible to brains and skill, allied with guts and determination'.

The storm had been the great test of all these. Another, minor, almost trivial, but supremely irritating test followed, organised, with the best of intentions, by the War Office. Once again, Lt.Col. Cowan's team rose to the occasion, as he himself describes.

When the storm was over we had a visitation from some high ranking Officers from the War Office. They were fresh, clean, washed, had polished boots, smelt nice and were full of praise; charming fellows. We liked and welcomed them, except one, let us call him Colonel Snodgrass (this was not his name) who was critical, asked awkward questions, why we had not done so and so, and to make things worse, he was sometimes right.

We hated him; and we could see that Wally Walter, Mais and Gilbert disliked him even more. They wanted to be left alone to get some sleep. They became testy, we suffered, and something had to be done.

We had erected, in a beautifully selected site, at the foot of a steep shrub covered bank, with a fine view seawards, a small 'convenience' or (as they are called today) a toilet. It had a corrugated iron roof.

Now, even at this time, there were occasional loud noises as German fighter bombers broke through the anti-aircraft screen, dropped their bombs and scuttled off. (I recall that Andrew Hinrich's Company actually shot down a Focke-Wulf 190 with a Bren gun).

Colonel Snodgrass was sternly warned of these dangers and advised to take cover at once whenever he heard the warning siren.

Budworth, Barton and Jones took up their positions in the bushes at the top of the bank and waited.

Nature being what it is, it was only a matter of time before the Colonel, with a casual look around, slipped into the little hut. After a suitable, carefully timed and rehearsed interval Budworth cranked the handle of the klaxon horn, a terrible and frightening sound and Barton lobbed a large stone on to the corrugated iron roof with a crash; Jones shouted 'Take Cover'.

The result exceeded their wildest expectations — the door flew open and Colonel Snodgrass hobbled out with short steps, his cavalry breeches around his ankles, to fling himself full length face downwards into a slit trench — thoughtfully excavated close-by. As he lay there the gentle south west wind lifted his shirt tails to expose his white posterior.

There was silence, a group of officers nearby chatting together, a scene of absolute peace and quiet as the Colonel opened his tightly shut eyes and looked up. Captain Witcomb hurried to him, crying in concern, 'My dear Colonel, whatever is the matter. Are you all right?'

Colonel Snodgrass left that afternoon and was never seen again. Peace and tranquillity returned to Mulberry.

The lesson — never tell exhausted men how they should have carried out a job, even if you know you are right. If you do, you will, like the Colonel, regret it.

Those 'gentlemen in England, now abed' already referred to by Arthur Hirst when the invasion began, had both time and leisure to ponder the damage that the storm had done. Sir Bruce White had, he claims, foreseen that the Bombardons might become a cause of major danger, and had warned the Prime Minister of his apprehensions. In the account that follows, Allan Beckett makes it clear that Sir Bruce White was most certainly apprehensive about the performance of the Bombardons well in advance of D-day, as he had especially alerted Beckett to observe them.

I have been asked what I did at Arromanches, as I was obviously a supernumerary from the War Office without any specific job. My first interest was of course the Whale project as I had had a good deal of responsibility for its design. It was with great relief that I witnessed the ease and speed with which it could be set up once the tows arrived. Of course I made sure that the roadways were properly moored and enjoyed the greatest possible co-operation from Sainsbury in this respect.

I had plenty of time also to observe the behaviour of the spud pontoons, Phoenix caisson breakwaters and Bombardons. The failure of all the Bombardons came as no surprise because, prior to D-day, I had been asked by Bruce White to assess the suitability of their moorings, and I had reported them to be far too weak under the assumptions for wave pressure I used for the floating bridge. Eventually I assisted Sainsbury in sinking, by Piat mortar, one of the Bombardons that had broken adrift, collided with and breached the Phoenix breakwater, then entered the harbour creating the risk of even greater damage.

The power of the sea in a storm was evident even within the breakwaters of Mulberry B. I witnessed the driving ashore on to rocks of a Rhino pontoon fully loaded with company transport and other equipment. The whole of the pontoon and its cargo was beaten into a shapeless mass of twisted steel and sheet metal. The only easily recognisable part of the deck cargo that remained was the rubber-tyred-wheels which had become detached because their axles broke. The whole of this destruction took place in little more than 3 hours.

Whilst Mulberry B survived the storm on D+13 with only minor damage, the destruction by sea action at Mulberry A was total. The beach was littered with wrecked vessels piled one on top of another. It seemed to me that had these vessels put out to sea instead of relying on protection from the breakwater they would not have been lost. Basically, the Phoenix breakwaters failed due to overtopping whereupon all except one of the spud pontoon pier-head units became damaged beyond repair. The floating bridge behaved like a great net collecting all forms of miscellaneous craft which sawed through such moorings as had been laid. However the floating bridge itself was not too badly damaged and I was asked to act as liaison officer for its repair and transfer to Mulberry B[17] to make good the losses sustained in cross Channel towing during the storm. This was done, and in the end we had in Mulberry B more floating bridge equipment than we could use. I was interested to find that the one spud pontoon that had survived the storm at Mulberry A did so because the operator, despite instructions to the contrary and red light warnings of rope overload, had raised the pontoon well clear of the sea surface.

On reporting back to War Office on the performance of Mulberry B during the storm of D+13, I was asked by Bruce White how the Phoenix breakwater units behaved in Mulberry B. These I had watched during the storm and I described how some failures resulted from overtopping by long period waves. In such cases the seaward concrete walls fell outwards, as if driven by hydraulic internal pressure far in excess of that which might be attributed to wave height.

As to the behaviour of the spud moored pierhead pontoons, I reported that where pontoons were immediately downwind of the open harbour entrance the spud controlling cable had failed. In other words where the pierhead pontoons were protected by the breakwater they sustained no serious damage. Also there was at least one instance where a spud was

---

[17] See Cowan's account on page 141.

broken clean off below water level. The pontoon was removed to a less exposed position and a tug holed itself on the below-water broken spud then quickly sank out of sight. At low tide I looked for eddies that might indicate the location of the wreck, but eventually found it by hitting it with the bottom of my MTL! I laid a buoy, then reported the matter to the Naval Officer in charge who encircled my buoy with three green wreck markers at a suitable distance. My MTL was making unhappy engine noises so we beached her and found a bent propeller shaft. Fortunately we carried a spare shaft and after replacement the vessel was as good as new.

I have been asked to give my impression on the success or otherwise of the Mulberry harbours as a military undertaking, not only in the role of the designer of some of the equipment but as an observer of its use in warfare.

First, one must accept that the sea conditions under a strong on-shore wind can cause far more damage than enemy action, so that the value of breakwaters has to be a prime consideration.

In this respect the blockships were an unqualified success. They are quick and easy to get to site and, when expertly handled, little trouble to sink in position. The cost is of course high and the substitute in the form of Phoenix concrete caissons was effective in enlarging the area under protection from wave action. There is difficulty in compromising the necessary weight for stability with buoyancy for flotation and structural strength to resist wave pressure. In the open topped version of the Phoenix they failed when long period-waves spilled over the caisson wall. However with some patching up they served their purpose in Mulberry B. This cannot be said for Mulberry A.

The floating breakwaters (code named Bombardon) were a complete failure, due to insufficient strength in their design, and inadequate moorings at site. Even worse, their manufacture had jeopardised supply of thin steel plate which was indispensable for the making of small landing craft and pontoons. The spud pontoon pier heads worked well but their instructed mode of operation required that only part of the weight of the pontoon be applied to the spuds, because the weight of deck cargo and concrete gravity fenders when added to that of the pontoon exceeded the capacity of the spud control cables. This meant that the protection of the breakwater was vital to the success of the pier head. Where the breakwaters were less than fully efficient, the spud pontoons failed. This happened totally in Mulberry A, except in one case where the pontoon deck was empty, and the whole pontoon was jacked up above sea level. On Mulberry B the few failures were limited to an area behind the main entrance through the breakwater.

The floating bridge roadway, if properly moored and supported on
steel pontoons, appeared to be indestructible by wave action, but suffered
from collision by craft out of control.

Amidst the chaos, there was room for humour too. In his account of the storm, Sir
Alan Harris, a Captain who had been sent to Port-en-Bessin, the joint
American/British petrol port, on D+2, in command of the advance party of
933 Port Construction & Repair Company RE gives us this insight

> So it went on, for four nights and three days; desperate manoeuvres at
> night, hampered by the nauseous smoke screen, dangerous salvage
> attempts by day. Miraculously, 7000 tons of stores were landed safely
> during that period and even on the worst day some 800 tons (mostly
> ammunition) were got ashore. Calm weather came on June 23rd, (D+17).
> Mulberry A was lost but by and large Mulberry B had survived — its
> necessary repair heroically completed in just a few days.
>
> But not all was grimly heroic, not all the time. One day, one of our
> diving boats was working alongside a pierhead, when a Captain RASC
> hailed the crew yelling 'We dropped a crate of whisky hereabouts. If you
> can salvage it you can have a bottle'. Not Sergeant Walker's idea of the
> odds. He dived, came up and said 'Sorry, Sir; I saw a crate of cheese
> which I didn't think you would want, but no whisky'. The boat then
> motored away to a safe distance where a rope left dangling negligently
> over the bows was hauled up — crate attached. By the time I got on
> board the party was in full swing and old man Vicquelin, the skipper, was
> in a deplorable state; Scotland's answer to Calvados had been amply
> demonstrated.
>
> In spite of events you could not stop Vicquelin and his like from
> fishing, and mackerel formed a welcome change from compo rations: I
> didn't fancy them myself; they had an odd taste. Remember that the lip of
> the sea was filthy with all the refuse of war — ammo boxes, ration packs,
> strange pallid stringy objects, sometimes with khaki cloth or webbing
> attached. Some there were who went for a swim, but I could not wade
> through all that and enjoy it.

There are many separate, yet remarkably similar accounts of the storm. In each of
them, one fact is reiterated: Mulberry B survived, damaged but reparable; Mulberry
A suffered total 'demise', it was destroyed 'by sea action', it became a scene of
'devastation', it was 'destroyed and abandoned', it was 'destroyed beyond repair'.
Why should this have happened?

We have few reports from men who took part in assembling and operating
Mulberry A, but some facts can be deduced from what we have. A copy of *The
Bulldozer* for October 27th 1944 reports on the task of the Seabees in transporting,

assembling and placing the pre-fabricated harbours, and of their success in landing a record weight of munitions and supplies.

Supplies Pour in Through Synthetic Seabee Harbors

Over 17 million tons of munitions and supplies — more than twice the entire amount used by the AEF in 1917–1918 — were landed in France during the first 109 days of the invasion at the two pre-fabricated ports which had been built in Britain, towed across the rough channel, and set up under the noses, and guns, of the Nazis. According to dispatches received here, Seabees were instrumental in the transporting of these ready-made ports, as well as in their construction and placing.

In building these harbors, it was first necessary to scuttle 60 old ships to form the basic breakwaters. Then came the huge caissons of concrete and steel, some weighing more than 6,000 tons, which had been towed over by 85 seagoing tugs in an operation lasting three days and nights. In addition to the massive amount of materiel unloaded at these spots, 2 ½ million men and 500,000 vehicles (at the rate of four a minute, day and night, for 109 days) were also put ashore there. Until this news was released recently, the Germans, as well as the world at large, were curious as to how these totals of men and supplies managed to be landed on the French coast, inasmuch as the only known port there, Cherbourg, had been more or less destroyed. The secret of pre-fabricated ports was the secret of the 'miracle' of supply.

This report concentrated on success, and therefore omitted mention of the storm. Another report by Ken Ringle of the Washington Post Service, writing from England (undated), says in his article *When distant Harbors Ruled the Waves*

Half the pier sections intended for Mulberry A [sic] were lost in rough seas on the way over. The first units arrived off Omaha Beach on June 7, and three of the block ships were sunk in place for the northern breakwater that afternoon. The following day the first caisson arrived. The block-ship breakwater was completed June 10, despite being targetted sporadically by German artillery fire. The first ships docked at Mulberry A pier six days later, three days ahead of schedule. Mulberry B, in the British sector at Arromanches, was less than half finished. The first LST at the Mulberry dock discharged 78 vehicles — its entire load — in just 38 minutes. In the 11 additional hours it would have spent on the beach drying out, it could now return to England to load up again and be halfway back. The cargo capacity of the invasion beaches had suddenly more than doubled. By June 18, with its third dock still uncompleted, Omaha Beach had landed 197,444 troops, 27,340 vehicles and 68,799 tons of supplies. Mulberry A was not only living up to its projections, it was now the busiest port in all of Europe.

Then disaster struck.

On June 19, during an unusually high spring tide, the winds stiffened, backing to the north-east, and blew from the one point on the compass that built the waves over 100 miles of open water and aimed them into the harbor entrance. It was the worst summer storm in the channel for 40 years. It blew for four days. When it was over 21 of 35 caissons in one breakwater had capsized or been beaten in and the piers and docks were little more than twisted wreckage. The British Mulberry, still uncompleted and partially protected by the capes north of Le Havre, survived with little damage. Appalled by the damage at Omaha, Allied planners decided to move any salvageable parts of Mulberry A to Arromanches. The discharge of cargo had virtually stopped during the storm, and shortages ashore were becoming critical. Fortunately, Cherbourg was captured June 26, but it was another 20 days before its harbor could be cleared of wreckage and booby traps and allow the first ships to unload. Meanwhile, supply logistics were rebuilt around the intensified beaching and drying out of LSTs at Omaha plus the operation of a finally finished and greatly storm-reinforced Mulberry B at Arromanches. For all the immense expense and effort that went into the Mulberrys, the 'British Report to the Chiefs of Staff' on D-day suggested they were a waste of steel and labor and said the invasion could probably have succeeded without them. General Dwight D Eisenhower's chief of staff, General Walter Bedell Smith, however strongly disagreed. Though the Mulberrys may have only contributed 15 percent to the flow of needed material to the invasion forces, he said after the war, 'that 15 percent was crucial'.

This report seems to suggest that Mulberry B was in a more protected position than Mulberry A (which was largely true), but also that its incomplete state had saved it from further damage.

Another Seabee account is given by Raymond B Dierkes, of St. Louis, USA. His account is vivid, but laconic in the extreme, taking only two paragraphs to describe his experiences (in the 108th Section) of the journey to Normandy, the erection of the harbour and the storm. His story starts in Southampton.

Each morning the tug would pull us out and we would lower the spuds to the ocean floor and then we raised them. This one evening I thought it was odd to be pulled from berth, and we kept going, and going. This was June 4th.

The mates asked Mr Siegelman, 'what gives?' and he said, 'The time has come for us to do the job we were training for'. Boy did they all get sombre, especially being out in the Channel at night. The tug *Superman* pulled us and then on the 5th we looked up and you could walk across all those planes and gliders. On the 6th we were about 10 miles out from shore when all the ships started shelling the far shore. It lit up all the sky and I couldn't have imagined all these ships that I saw with their barrage balloons. We basically had a front row seat to the assault but then our Chief died of a heart attack. Chief Smith was in World War 1 and he was in his late 40s. The mates rolled him into a tarpaulin and he was removed later on the 6th.

We saw the breakwater form and the blockships sunk to form more breakwaters. Finally on the 7th the tug pulled us in farther where our spuds would hold us and left to do other work. We were visited by the Germans every night at 11 p.m. and we would hear shrapnel across our steel deck which really made some noise. Each day we could see the harbor taking shape, and it was these mates of mine that were doing the job. Finally 406 and 407 were set up about two and a half miles out from shore, and Capt. Clark wanted the harbour to operate by June 17th. Well we were operating by June 15th and everyone clapped when the 1st LST came up to unload. Each ship after that got easier and easier to the point that the ship would be unloaded in less than an hour and head back to England. We were operating four and a half days and then this storm came and shut us down. After the storm we at Omaha Beach were dismantled, but Utah Beach kept going. I believe we made a difference as the breakwater stayed intact, except for a couple of 'coffins' breaking up. We were towed back to Falmouth and within a week we turned our Pierhead over to the English Army.

Members of the British forces also give accounts of the destruction at Omaha Beach, and the possible reasons for this, so that it becomes a rather clearer picture. Vice Admiral Hickling, who has already been quoted, admits that Mulberry B survived partly because 'we had the protection of the Calvados Shoal', but adds 'but that was by no means the only reason why the British harbour survived'.

Sir Bruce White, who received daily bulletins during the construction of both harbours, seems to have been slightly disturbed by the difference in the speeds of assembly.

From the reports, I deduced that, while the British harbour was proceeding according to plan, the American Mulberry was being constructed much more quickly. The result was that the American Mulberry was brought into operation earlier than the British.

Sir Bruce was also concerned about the placing and the capabilities of the breakwater units, usually called Phoenix.

While every step had been taken to ascertain the nature of the seabed on which the harbour would be founded, including very hazardous reconnaissance by mini-submarines, we could not be definite and therefore tendered a measure of caution in founding the breakwater units.

> The units were designed for a short period of summer weather and were
> open-topped, although they had the necessary freeboard.

In his assessment of the effects of the storm, Maj. Gen. Sir Harold Wernher arrives
at an identical opinion for the destruction of the American harbour.

> By early September, the British *Mulberry* port was well-established, but
> the American port had been destroyed owing to:
> (a) the rapidity with which the American Army endeavoured to erect it
>   and
> (b) the fact that proper soundings were not taken and many of the
>   *Phoenixes* were sunk out of sight.
>
> I had anticipated the latter occurring and suggested to Admiral
> Ramsay that the British, having manufactured the American *Mulberry*,
> should be responsible for placing it into position. Ramsay replied that
> there was not sufficient British personnel to carry out the task and,
> although he disliked the idea, it was unavoidable that the Americans
> would have to take care of their own port.

Brigadier Walter, whose friendly rivalry with Captain A D Clark of the US Navy,
in command of the American Force 128, was brought to an abrupt end when the
storm struck, apportions no blame, but praises the American attitude to the disaster,
and their willingness to help with vitally needed components for Mulberry B.

> A day or two after we surfaced from the great storm starting on 19 June, I
> went over to Omaha beach with Mais to see the Americans at Mulberry A
> and we were quite shattered by what we found. Mulberry B was bent and
> damaged — but it was obvious to us that Mulberry A was finished and it
> brought no joy whatsoever that the Royal Engineers had survived and
> won, because we were all on the same side and both harbours were
> needed for the build-up of the landings. The high command soon decided
> to abandon Mulberry A and to transfer to Mulberry B such remaining
> units of breakwater and floating roadways as were left in the UK. As bad
> luck would have it an exceptional number of tows had sailed from the UK
> on 19 June and many with their crews were lost on their way over during
> the storm. In the event we had not even enough to complete our Mulberry
> B. One enduring memory of the storm and this disaster was the
> wonderful way in which the Americans quickly got over their
> disappointment at their failure and set about enthusiastically to help us
> with our harbour in every way they could. The story of the storm has
> been well told by Ronnie Cowan, but I should like to pay special tribute
> to my opposite number — Captain Petrie — for his advice and guidance
> as the storm blew up — we did the right things because we had good
> sailors with us.

Colonel Harris expresses equal gratitude for the generosity of the Americans, though he seems to suspect some ulterior motive. He also, it should be noted, blames the Bombardons rather than the Phoenixes for the major damage to Mulberry A.

> What of Mulberry A? It had been smashed by the failure of the moorings of Bombardons which allowed these massive floating breakwaters to crash into the caisson breakwaters and, through them, into the pierheads and roadsteads in general. Mulberry A seemed to be finished. The decision by Eisenhower to allow all spares, all equipment and all personnel to be diverted to Mulberry B was very welcome and enthusiastically executed. Was it, however, motivated by the supposedly imminent fall of Cherbourg and also by a feeling of relief that Mulberry A had disappeared? In fact, it seems not to have done. Records have it that large quantities of stores were discharged through Mulberry A. How? Much mystery still surrounds the subject, but it seems that; a) further Phoenixes were sunk offshore to provide shelter; b) Liberty ships discharged in this shelter to huge numbers of DUKWs; c) the underlying rock of the beach was friable and could be bulldozed into a smooth surface on which Liberty ships, LSTs, etc. could ground and discharge directly onto shore transport. Delay due to tide was inevitable of course.

Other, possibly inflated claims, were made concerning the continued high volume of throughput through Mulberry A (although one could question whether or not it was still a Mulberry). Such claims were made again in a French documentary video, *The Mulberry Harbours* by Les Ports du Jour J/ACCANN. On viewing this in 1994, Brigadier Walter immediately challenged its likelihood. He did not mince his words

> At my meeting with the film producers on 5th Oct. 94, I was told that this story 'that the Americans discharged larger tonnages over Omaha Beach — without their destroyed Mulberry Harbour A — than the British did through their Mulberry B' *originated from unspecified American sources'*. Having failed to plant Mulberry A successfully, and maintain it through and after the storm, this statement is perhaps not an unexpected response. However, it is nonsense!
>
> The idea that you could discharge greater tonnages of stores, guns and tanks over a tidal beach with limited hours of use each day, than could be discharged over a 24 hour day through Mulberry B, with all its port facilities, pierheads, and floating roadways, including our ability to discharge and turn round a Landing Ship Tank (LST) in 23 minutes bears witness to the fatuousness of this remark.

It is not our place to arbitrate: each statement was, without doubt, made in full belief that it was accurate. In his most recent paper, *My Final Assessment*, Brigadier Walter gives his trenchant view on the survival of Mulberry B. In his opinion,

Mulberry B survived the storm because the British contingent took proactive measures to ensure its survival: every available kite anchor was collected for the purpose of stiffening the roadways; the pierheads were 'spudded' up to their maximum extent to prevent wave damage; Navy and Army vessels were mobilized to patrol the harbour to prevent stray craft from damaging the piers and roadways (there were 100–200 craft sheltering in Mulberry B following the storm; the numbers vary between accounts). These protective patrols were vital. On one occasion Brigadier Walter drew his pistol to induce a crew to sink their craft.

In the same paper, Brigadier Walter tells us that Mulberry A failed for the following reaons: owing to a decision to enlarge their harbour, the Americans sank their Phoenix units in deeper water which reduced their freeboard and led to their collapse (there is almost universal agreement that unrestrained Bombardons also contributed to the demise of Phoenixes); they failed to stiffen their roadways (Allan Beckett has reported that they did not have their full complement of anchors); the vital control of loose craft in the harbour broke down. As Walter puts it: 'All that was left of the harbour were the blockships.'

Brigadier Walter's statement about the importance of the numbers of anchors used on the pontoons is substantiated by Professor Sir Alan Harris in his Dickinson Lecture. He explains precisely how the floating roadways were anchored, and what the holding power of the anchors was. He then says

> At Mulberry B it worked; at Mulberry A, due to a complicated series of misunderstandings and misinformation, the floating roadways had only one anchor cable every six pontoons instead of one each. This contributed to the failure.

Sir Alan's concise (or, as he says, 'bare') account of the storm and its aftermath is one of the clearest we have, and it is worth quoting here in its entirety. He does not criticise possible defects in the organisation of Mulberry A, but concentrated on the excellent and, in the event, vitally necessary, precautions taken at Mulberry B as soon as the storm warning was received.

> It is a slight exaggeration to say that this harbour was in service a fortnight after landing, but a gale blew from the morning of D+13 (19th June) until the night of D+19 (22nd June), direction north to north-east, force 6–7 most of the time; waves were a mean height of 8–9 ft. with a maximum of 12–14 ft. The depression was not intense nor were the winds tempestuous, but they blew from the same quarter for four days and, with a fetch of 100 miles, stirred up a dangerous sea.
>
> Said Wavell to Liddell-Hart: 'If I were to write military history, I would concentrate on the actualities of war — fatigue, hunger, fear, lack of sleep, weather, inaccurate information, the time factor and so forth.'

Only those who were there can speak of the actualities of those four days. What happened, however must be told in bare (and oh! how bare!) fact.

Here, surely, was the answer to the enemy's dearest wish — heavy weather onshore before consolidation of the beach-head; at least a relief of pressure, perhaps the opportunity of total repulse.

The Meteorological warning was short; the depression came up from the Mediterranean, not from, as is usual, the Atlantic; the Met. People, without weather stations to the east, were blind in that quarter.

Action was immediate. Lt. Col. Mais ordered all floating roadway moorings to be checked, harbour tugs to be fuelled and victualled fully and to be ready to grapple and tow away craft out of control; parties of Sappers to be allocated to various emergency tasks, orders to be given to fire on any craft attempting to come alongside pierheads, pontoons, etc., all craft to windward of the pierheads and piers to up-anchor and move to leeward. Warning shots were fired by the Bofors cannon on the Phoenix (reputed to be more dangerous than the Luftwaffe, they had already punched holes in the funnel of HMS *Rodney*); Capt. Witcomb, officer in charge of pierheads, was told to hoist the pierheads up the Spuds as far as he dared.

Mulberry was intended to provide shelter for 1000 small craft in case of storm. The direction of the wind brought such refugees in at the eastern end; holding ground was bad; most were equipped with anchors much less efficient than the Kite — and the Beetles in deeper water were mostly of the more fragile concrete sort. To be awakened by some soldier with orders to sling the hook and move somewhere else (orders supported by dire threats) was not welcomed by skippers who, after a rough night at sea, had finally found shelter.

Most damage was done by just such craft hitting the LST pierhead and floating pier and the easterly Spud pontoons. A Landing Craft (Tank) (LCT), crewless, doors swinging, struck a stores pierhead and was smashing both itself and the pierhead to pieces, when out of the murk came the tugs, some British, some American, who grappled and towed it away. Capt. John Luck, RE, (Officer in charge of British tugs) and John Heming with his American MTLs, by their skill and daring, saved the piers from destruction, times without number.

So it went on for four days and nights, desperate avoidance measures at night (in no way helped by the regular nauseous smokescreen), equally desperate repair attempts during the day. No one got much sleep, all continued despite total exhaustion; miraculously, over 7,000 tons of stores were nonetheless landed during that time; even on the worst day, 800 tons, mostly ammunition, was got ashore.

Calmer weather came on D+17 (23rd June) and damage could be assessed. Stores piers were more or less reparable by replacement of some moorings and Beetle pontoons. LST pierheads and piers were in a bad way, but by remarkable efforts were back in service within a few days (some say two, some say four, but it wasn't long). There was damage to such Phoenix as were in more than 5 fathoms depth and some had slid around but, by and large, the breakwaters, both Phoenix and Gooseberry, was still in being, though needing attention.

What of the rest of the beach-head?

Mulberry A was abandoned save for the Gooseberry part, behind which stores continued to be landed on the beach, without benefit of pierheads and piers. All recoverable equipment of value to Mulberry B was brought over. Col. Bronson of the US Corps of Engineers, a close friend of Lt. Col. Mais, had already responded to an appeal for oxyacetylene burning gear; help had anticipated the decision by General Eisenhower to concentrate all Mulberry equipment on Mulberry B.

The beaches were everywhere littered with wrecked craft piled on each other, sometimes two or three deep; corpses too. Pessimistic eyes at HQ, viewing the air-photos, despaired of the invasion.

Nevertheless, however bad the situation at first appeared, the rate of recovery was remarkable, and humour was undimmed. The success of the Gooseberries, and the German attempt to improve propaganda were noted

I well remember Rear Admiral Vian sending Admiral Ramsay a signal in the middle of the great storm, 'The Gooseberries may save the day' and save it they did. The blockships were 100 percent efficient, and there they sit to this day practically undamaged and unmoved. Incidentally, we were amused to read the German communiqués that they claimed to have sunk all the blockships!

Sir Alan Harris gives the final summary.

There were two crucial moments, the gale and just after. The 7,000 tons landed during the gale kept the battle going, but immediately after the gale, when the whole coastline was tightly locked with sunken craft, it would have been dire straits for the invasion were it not for Mulberry.

The psychological factor is important. Men landing, seeing what had been prepared for them, went ashore with heads high. Those in the field were confident that supplies, supplies of anything, were easily available and that wounded would be rapidly evacuated.

Let the last word be French; Jean Merrien, in *Le Livres des Côtes de France* says 'Port Churchill d'Arromanches fut realisé, aux prix d'efforts prodigieux, et tint bon — sans quoi la face du monde aurait pu être changée.' Or, in English, 'Port churchill at Arromanches was brought to

being at the cost of prodigious efforts and held up — without which the
face of the world might have been changed.'

This, then, is the story of the storm and its aftermath told by those who experienced
it on the harbour. What happened to those who remained at sea throughout the
period, or to the one whose account we have who was travelling from England to
work in a Regimental First Aid Post at Bayeaux, when the storm broke?

First, what was it like to be in the crew of a tug, transporting Phoenixes, Whales
and Pontoon floats across the Channel? Here is an extract from *Seahorses of The
Tees'* by John Proud, published by Tees Towing Co., Ltd., in 1985.

> We are fortunate in having a diary of the movements of *Euston Cross*
> from the time she left Middlesborough on the 23rd May, 1944, under the
> command of Harry Page and with a crew of seventeen, until the
> 22nd September 1944. The diarist was Arthur Greenwell, then wireless
> operator, and now the Company's Commercial Director. His notes give a
> clear indication of how dangerous, hard and at times frustrating a job it
> was that faced them. When they set off they did not know their ultimate
> destination or for what purpose the units they were towing were to be
> used. The *Euston Cross* was to be away from her home river for nine
> months in all. The 'log' records briefly the 80-hour-long gale from the
> 19th to 22nd June which is referred to as 'heavy sea' and 'heavy swell' when
> in fact it was the worst summer-time storm in the Channel for forty years!
> It was so severe that the American artificial harbour was completely
> wrecked and so much damage was caused to the British harbour that the
> entire operation 'Overlord' was threatened with disaster. Skipper Harry
> Page was not to remain with the vessel throughout the invasion duties, as
> he had the misfortune to fall and injure his leg. His place was taken by
> Tommy Hutchinson.
>
> The assembly points for the individual harbour units were the River
> Thames, off Dungeness and off Selsey for the concrete 'Phoenix' units
> forming the breakwaters, and off Dungeness and in the Solent for the
> 'Whale' units which made-up the floating piers and roadways. *Euston
> Cross* was involved in all of these areas, as were *Charing Cross, Kings
> Cross* (1) and *Queens Cross.* The large crew of the Eus*ton Cross* will have
> been noted. Extra accommodation had been provided — in the rope
> locker aft! Included amongst the augmented crew were an additional
> wireless operator, a naval signaller and two DEMS gunners. These latter
> were to man the Oerlikon gun on the foredeck and also the Lewis gun.
> Rifles were also provided and the ship was fitted with anti-aircraft wire
> rope projectiles and bridge protective plating. Her appearance and trim
> had altered materially.

Let now the following extracts from the diary speak for themselves and, in doing so, pay tribute to all the tugmen who took part in this gigantic operation.

Extracts from the Log of the Movements of EUSTON CROSS
23rd May to 22nd September, *1944.*

23rd May	Left Tees with *Empire Sara,* 7.45 a.m., towing 'Donald Duck'. (A concrete 'Phoenix' unit.)
25th	Anchored Southend, 10 a.m.
26th	Still anchored in the Warp. Towed in by *Sun VIII* and beached at Southend. Rope in propeller.
27th	Propeller clear. Rejoined *Empire Sara* at Warp. Arrived Dungeness 6.00 a.m. Left 'Donald Duck', sailed for Portsmouth, arrived 6.30 p.m. turned round laid in Stokes Bay.
30th May	Laid alongside ss *Spanker* (1,875/1917), Stokes Bay.
1st June	Coaled. Watered at ms *Karabagh,* (6,590/1932). To Lee-on-Solent.
6th	Lee-on-Solent Invasion started. Picked up the bridge links. ('Whales')
7th June	12.30 p.m. sailed in convoy for France with bridge links.
8th	Cast bridge links adrift. Arrived off Caen 7 a.m. Anchored 2 miles from coast. Weighed anchor 9.35 p.m. Warship bombardment 7 to 7.30 p.m. Bayeaux captured, 6½ miles from where we anchored. 11.45 p.m. ship shelled and sunk; believe it to be one of four enemy destroyers.
9th	Dropped anchor 12.30 a.m. Weighed anchor 6 a.m. Picked up bridge link off Nab and towed to Lee-on-Solent. Anchored 11.10 p.m.
10th	Watered and coaled. On board ms *Aorangi* for an hour. Port hole repaired.
11th	Sailed 5.50 a.m. for France with *Dundas* towing pontoon bridge.
12th	Arrived off Isigny 6p.m. ¼ mile off-shore Grandchamp. Set off 8.30 p.m. 11.45 p.m. stopped by shot across bows from Torpedo Boats.
13th	Anchored 1.30 a.m. Under weigh 6 a.m. Arrived Lee-on-Solent 5.15 p.m. Watered at ms *British Faith,* (6,977/1928). Anchored near *Aorangi*

	Watered at *Karabagh*. Picked pontoon float up at St. Helen's towed to Peel Bank.
18th	Coaled at ss *Skerbrook* (1,979/1922). Anchored. Moved Thames *III* to *British Faith,* Sailed light 2.30 p.m. for France. Heavy sea. Arrived 1 a.m. Heavy swell. Grounded whilst trying to connect to American ship. Damaged rudder. Taken in tow at 11 a.m. by *Empire Rupert*. Heavy sea still running.
21st	Passed Spithead Gateway 10.30 a.m. To Lee-on-Solent.
26th June	Left Lee-on-Solent in tow of HMS *Resolve* at 11 a.m. Anchored at St. Helen's Bay at noon. Under weigh 2 p.m. bound for Southend.

Despite the laconic (and entirely correct) tone of the log in noting 'heavy sea' twice, we can deduce that the conditions were extremely bad, and the ensuing damage to the *Euston Cross* so severe that her repairs at Grimsby took over six weeks to complete, even allowing for the fact that there was vital need for tugs, and that she would have been given as much priority as possible.

Richard Polglaze was still aboard the old 1935 Clyde paddle steamer *Talisman*, refitted as an Anti-aircraft ship by the Admiralty and renamed *Aristocrat*. On D-day she had ferried many of the top-ranking officers to France, becoming their first HQ at Arromanches. After more permanent HQs had been appointed, *Aristocrat* took on the duties of convoy routing and anti-aircraft protection. The onset of the storm found the old ship in harbour at Mulberry B. Polglaze continues the story

> In the early hours of 19 June (D+13) there was a sudden drop in barometric pressure and the wind began to blow up from the north-east. We were actually lying inside the harbour at the time and soon received a signal ordering us to leave as the sheltered water was needed for protection of the hundreds of DUKWS, small landing craft, tugs and pontoons. Within hours the storm reached gale force 8, gusting up to force 9 at times. Captain Bowman feared our anchor would not hold in such conditions and as we were off a lee shore he decided the safest course would be to weigh anchor and steam out the gale. For 72 hours *Aristocrat* cruised up and down the coast. Each time she turned all the crockery would rattle and pots pans and utensils go flying around the messes. Under such conditions little could be done in the way of cooking in the galley so we had to exist on emergency rations – corned beef, herrings in tomato and similar delicacies. Most of the old 3 badge seamen stayed on upper deck level, retreating into their stores and workshops to sleep; we, being younger and less experienced, didn't really appreciate the danger.

Looking back, I don't recall there being much seasickness but it certainly was an experience.

Aristocrat, originally intended to spend her life in the sheltered waters of the Firth of Clyde and Kyles of Bute, weathered the storm very well indeed, which says a great deal for her builders and, I must add, for Lt. Commander Bowman in the way he handled her under such extreme conditions. She had undoubtedly taken a severe pounding and confirmed to the hilt her reputation of being an excellent sea-boat. We thus had a great admiration and sympathy for the minesweeper crews who had to carry on sweeping in ships much smaller that *Aristocrat* and regardless of weather conditions. As far as I can remember *Aristocrat* never suffered any paddle wheel failures while in service, which was quite remarkable considering how low she sat in the water with all the additional plating, armament and equipment. I am told one reason for this was that the power output of her machinery was automatically reduced when the current in the propulsion motor reached a certain value. When the wheels became choked with water she would immediately ease off and then surge forward again when they cleared.

When the wind finally abated, as quickly as it had sprung up, we returned to harbour and saw the havoc the storm had caused. Hundreds of vessels had been damaged and the beaches were littered with landing craft and other ships which had been blown ashore, including HMS *Fury*, a destroyer previously damaged by a mine and now lifted onto the beach beneath the cliffs. Some of the port construction had also suffered damage, but we later learned that Mulberry 'A' Harbour on the American sector had been much more badly damaged and had been abandoned. In fact, apart from a small amount of ammunition, all landing had ceased during the storm and matters were becoming critical for the troops ashore when, much to their relief, the wind suddenly abated. From the early days of the landings many captains had discovered that they were able to beach their ships to off-load, so new procedures were followed and the delivery of stores and ammunition was quickly resumed.

This story is a remarkable tribute to the design and construction of the old Clyde paddle steamers, some of which remain in service at the time of writing.

Our final account of the storm comes from a sister in the QAIMNS. (Queen Alexandra's Imperial Military Nursing Service), Barbara Lane, now Mrs. Scott-Jupp. Her story, as with all those we have quoted so far, shows a courage and determination which, with an unshakeable sense of the ridiculous, carried these brave women through a terrible journey.

We had heard on the news about the D-day Landings and wondered when we would be required over there. We had been trained to put up tents in 20 minutes, packed the whole hospital and its equipment into

2-man loads, and now our British General Hospital was a mobile 600 beds unit to act at first as a large Regimental First Aid Post.

The casualties were to be treated and patched up as possible, each man given one injection of Tetanus and one of Penicillin and then air-lifted to Britain. Those who couldn't be evacuated were sent to Theatre, where an exhausted staff worked 24 hours a day in shifts, and then moved on when possible. As we were only a few miles behind the front line, which at that time was Caen, this meant that any casualty which could be air-lifted could be in a military British hospital within a few hours, which undoubtedly saved many lives.

While we were waiting for our orders, we were part of a huge military and naval encampment — American, French, Poles, Norwegians, camouflaged under trees at a top secret site, not allowed to leave camp, 'Somewhere in the South of England', so secret, in fact, that to this day I have no idea where we were.

At last our orders came. Reveille was at 4 a.m. and we were having a hasty breakfast before departure, when we heard the doodlebug cut out its engine as always before descent, and dived for cover. This one passed over very low, knocked off one of the chimneys, but luckily exploded just on the other side of a small hut behind the house, and no-one was hurt. Not a very auspicious start to the day.

Shaken but not stirred, dressed in battledress, puttees and boots, duffel bag, bed rolls, mess tins etc., etc., we loaded ourselves and all the hospital equipment into lorries and joined a huge convoy for embarkation to Southampton. Several cheerless hours later we embarked and were duly billeted into the lowest level of the troopship which had been a cross channel steamer, and the more fortunate men were higher up the scale. This was explained to us reasonably and gently, that women were more expendable than men at this juncture, as we were not fighters!! Though bound to agree in principle it was little comfort to us.

We were scarcely out to sea when a (very severe) storm blew up which lasted for about 3 days. We were moored off the coast near Arromanches and there were so many vessels almost side by side anchored around us, that you could nearly step from one to the other. They were all waiting to unload supplies to the beleaguered troops in France who had had no reinforcement for those stormy days. Water supplies got lower and lower until we were rationed to one pint per day for drinking, washing and teeth. German bombers flew sorties overhead from time to time, causing some anxiety, but the RAF were wonderful and brilliant in their defence of our ships.

On the evening of the third day, the sea became a little calmer and every ship began trying to disembark their much needed supplies. We women were duly marshalled in front of the RSM who informed us that

(a) we were to disembark by scrambling nets to waiting land crafts, that
(b) we were to instantly obey his command to jump and do it p.d.q. If we
failed to do so, he predicted all sorts of broken bones, as he would time
our jumps to coincide with the rise and fall of the landing craft in the big
swell. So suitably subdued, and not a little apprehensive, having never
seen landing nets, let alone go down them, we lined up on deck and were
helped over the side. It was a scary experience, as our weighty, fully
equipped selves pressed the nets against the ship and it was difficult to
get a good toe-hold. However, down we went, encouraged from above
and below, and near the bottom took one terrified look at the plunging
landing craft and our RSM looking grimmer than ever, and when he said
'Jump', we jumped, landing in a relieved heap on the craft. Everyone
made it, bar a few small casualties and we set off for the Mulberry which
was heaving gently up and down in the swell.

As we went ashore there were cheers, catcalls and whistles from all
the naval ships and a great welcome from everyone. A loud tannoy came
across the water from the Command ship, 'Will the occupants of landing
craft 7 please hide their faces — you are distracting my men,' which was
received with even louder cheers. Apart from our welcome there was an
eerie silence — no guns, no planes, and we couldn't help think of the
carnage and suffering endured by so many at this exact spot not so many
days ago.

We landed, and were rushed along Mulberry and cleared the beach as
quickly as possible as they were expecting the nightly strafing at 7 p.m.
We just made it and jumped into trenches until the raid was past, then
boarded lorries and went swiftly on the road to Bayeux.

On arrival we were taken to an empty chateau on the edge of the
town, told not to venture outside as there had been no time to sweep for
booby traps, and bedded down for the night in the ballroom.

Next day we dug ourselves into an orchard, unpacked the 2-man
loads and prepared for our first casualties and the rhythm of receiving,
patching up, operating and injecting for which we were called and
trained.

One of the two men who had longed, but had been unable to be present in
Normandy on D-day itself, was at last able to visit the area. This was in July, 1944,
just after the storm, and Sir Winston Churchill saw all there was to be seen both on
land, and in the air from General Montgomery's captured Fieseler Storch aeroplane.
His last visit was to the field hospital, already fully operational.

Finally I went to the field hospital, where, though it was a quiet day, a
trickle of casualties was coming in. One poor man was to have a serious
operation, and was actually on the table about to take the anaesthetic. I
was slipping away, when he said he wanted me. He smiled wanly and

kissed my hand. I was deeply moved, and very glad to learn later on that the operation had been entirely successful.

Well pleased with all he had seen, he returned to the UK on 23rd July, and on 25th July sent the tribute he felt was due to the 'naval officer in charge of Arromanches', then Captain, later Vice Admiral, Hickling. This read:

> I send you and all under your command my warmest congratulations on the splendid work that has been done at Arromanches. This miraculous port has played, and will continue to play, a most important part in the liberation of Europe. I hope to pay you another visit before long.
>
> The above message should be promulgated to all concerned, in such a way that it does not become known to the enemy, who are as yet ignorant of the capacity and potentialities of Arromanches.

This tribute is a fitting one to all those who planned, built, transported, planted and used Mulberry, as well as to those who, like the QAIMNS, had an auxiliary, but no less vital rôle in the whole adventure.

CONCLUSION

In future years at gatherings and parties you will meet many men who will claim to have served at Mulberry B and built the harbour. You must say nothing, just let them talk and you will know that they boast this way because they wish they had been with us. You have the knowledge that it was you who were here and that against the odds you built the harbour at Arromanches. Nothing and no one can take this proud memory away from you.

— Brigadier Walter's farewell to his officers at Mulberry

In December 1944, Sir Walter Monckton began his analysis of the Mulberry harbours. He and his staff conducted interviews for several months before the report was finally published in September 1945. His task was a difficult one and, reading the evidence, there is considerable conflict of opinion concerning the success, or otherwise, of the various components.

At the time the report was drafted, this was more than mere accounting. The Japanese war was still on and serious consideration was being given to the use of artificial ports in the Far East. Despite the conflicting accounts, a consensus seems to have emerged:

- Blockships were definitely a good thing and would be used again without hesitation, although some reinforcement of the superstructure was recommended

- Phoenix units did a good job but their construction was not ideally suited to the environment. The modification to provide 'swim ends' had a marginal benefit in terms of towability but also encouraged basal scour as the ends created gaps between the units. The addition of decking to later models was an improvement but lack of strength in tension, despite metal reinforcement, was a problem

- Whale piers and roadways were useful but in the opinion of some not essential except for the handling of awkward and heavy loads such as bulldozers. They also came into their own for the evacuation of casualties. The decision to use concrete for the beetles was widely criticised

- Everyone was impressed with abilities and usefulness of the DUKWs

- No one had anything good to say about Bombardons

- Any plans to deploy a floating harbour in the Far East based on the 'tow and assemble' Mulberry model were out of the question without extensive design changes and on-site manufacture of certain components, e.g. Phoenix.

It is of course easy to generalise, but any reading of Sir Walter's papers would bring these conclusions to light[18]. As we saw in an earlier chapter, the storm was the sternest test of both men and equipment; the disruption and overcrowding that it caused within the breakwater reflected badly on Mulberry in general. But, as we have seen in this book through the eyes of those that were there, Mulberry was a remarkable achievement against all the odds. *The Times* newspaper on 25th January, 1945, carried the following:

> Mr Bevin, reviewing the building of munition works, the extensive preparations for the reception of the great American armies, and the building of the Mulberry artificial harbours, said he thought the employers' and operatives' federations ought to compile the history of their industry in the war. He estimated that the use of the Mulberries, instead of fighting to capture existing docks, must have saved the British and American Armies from 100,000 to 150,000 casualties.

In June 1944, Sir Winston Churchill wrote this to President Roosevelt:

> I had a jolly day on Monday on the beaches and inland. There is a great mass of shipping extended more than fifty miles along the coast. It is being increasingly protected against weather by the artificial harbours, nearly every element of which has been a success, and will soon have effective shelter against bad weather.
>
> . . . You used the word 'stupendous' in one of your early telegrams to me. I must admit that what I saw could only be described by that word, and I think your officers would agree as well. The marvellous efficiency of the transportation exceeds anything that has ever been known in war.

In conclusion, we turn once more to Maj. General Sir Harold Wernher, and a letter that he wrote to Sir Walter Monckton after receiving his report.

> *Dear Monckton,*
>
> *Thank you very much for the Report on 'Mulberry' which I am returning herewith. I should like to congratulate you on an admirable document. I know how difficult it has been to reconcile all the conflicting evidence.*
>
> *I am afraid all these things have been rendered obsolete by the Atomic Bomb, and in any case I do not think the 'Mulberry' was applicable to any operation other than one within 100 miles of this coast.*

---

[18] Copies of the Monckton Papers can be obtained from the Bodleian Library, Oxford.

I am appending a few remarks which I hope will be useful. I think it might be worthwhile drawing attention to the remarkable secrecy that was maintained in spite of the fact that so many people were involved, and that labour was scattered all over the country.

SELECTED REFERENCES

Beckett, Allan H: 'Some Aspects of the Design of Flexible Bridging, including Whale Floating Roadways', *The Civil Engineer in War*, 1948.

Brown, A & Polglaze, R: *HMS Aristocrat* (Waverley Excursions Ltd.).

Churchill, Sir Winston S: *The Second World War, Vol. VI, Triumph and Tragedy* (Cassell & Co. Ltd.).

Coughtrie, Thomas R: *From the Start of the Mulberry Project* (private account).

Cowan, Lt. Col. R J P: 'Notes on the Construction of Mulberry Harbour in Normandy, June–July 1944'. Lecture Imp Coll of Science & Technology, Dept of Civil Engineering, June 1975.

Harris, Sir A: 'The Mulberry Harbours', the 19th Dickinson Memorial Lecture, *Transactions of the Newcomen Society*, Volume 61, 1989–90.

Hartcup, G: *Code Name Mulberry* (David & Charles).

Hickling, Vice Admiral H: 'The Prefabricated Harbour'. *The Journal of the Royal United Service Institution,* Vol. XC, 1945.

McIntyre, Lt. H C: War Office Reports, 1943/4 (Ministry of Defence).

Monckton, Sir W: Private papers, Bodleian Library.

Shipyard Spotlight and *Shipbuilders & Shipping Record* (published by The Admiralty).

Murchie, A T: *The Mulberry Harbour Project in Wigtownshire 1942–1944* (G C Book Publishers Ltd.).

Scott-Bowden, Lt. Gen: 'COPP to Normandy 1943/44 — a Personal Account of Part of the Story'. *Royal Engineers Journal*. Vol. 108, 1994.

Walter, Brigadier A E M: *A Harbour Goes to France — Memories and Reflections* (privately published).

Wernher, Maj. Gen. Sir H: *World War II: Personal Experiences* (privately published), 1950.

White, Brigadier Sir Bruce G: *The artifical invasion harbours called Mulberry — A personal story by Sir Bruce White KBE* (privately published), 1980.

PERMISSIONS

Extracts from the accounts of Admiral Hickling: Reproduced by kind permission of Royal United Services Institute For Defence Studies.

Reproduction of Crown Copyright Material: Bigot © British Crown Copyright/MOD. Reproduced with the permission of Her Majesty's Stationery Office.

Lt. H C McIntyre Report: © British Crown Copyright/MOD. Reproduced with the permission of Her Majesty's Stationery Office.

Military Engineer [US]: Reproduced with permission of The Society of American Military Engineers (SAME), publisher and copyright holder.

New Civil Engineer material used in chapter Sheltered Water (page 79): With kind permission of *The New Civil Engineer*.

Extracts from *Code Name Mulberry* by kind permission of Guy Hartcup, published by David & Charles, 1977

Extracts from *Shipyard Spotlight* and *Shipbuilding & Shipping Records* are Naval Text.

Churchill's extracts 'Finally I went to the field hospital . . .': Reproduced with permission of Curtis Brown Ltd., London, on behalf of the Estate of Sir Winston S Churchill. Copyright Winston S Churchill 1954.

Extract of letter from HM King to Churchill: With kind permission from the Churchill Archives Centre, CHAR 20/136/10 , and The Royal Archives.

Excerpts from Wernher's Diary and letter to Monckton in Conclusion: Reproduced with kind permission of the family of the late Major General Sir Harold Wernher.

Extract from the *HMS Aristocrat:* With kind permission of Waverley Excursions Ltd., Glasgow.

Extracts from the reports of Brig. Bruce White: With kind permission of the family of the late Sir Bruce White.

Extracts from the account of Brig. A E M Walter: With kind permission of Brig. A E M Walter.

Extracts from the papers of Lt. Col. L Scott-Bowden; and Sir Alan Harris: With kind permission of the Royal Engineers Museum, Chatham.

Photograph of Spud Pontoon at Leith: By kind permission of The Motherwell Heritage Centre.

Extract from Alex. Findlay's of Motherwell: Reproduced with kind permission of William Lind, of the Ballast Trust, Johnstone.

Extract of John Proud's *Seahorses of the Tees:* Reproduced by kind permission of Cory Ship Towage Ltd.

Extract from the account of Lt. Col. R J P Cowan; Reproduced by kind permission of the Institution of Civil Engineering, London.

INDEX

Hartcup, Guy, vii, 31, 74, 79, 109, 167
Heming, John, xiv, 136, 137, 138, 139, 153
Hickling, Vice-Adm. H., CBE., DSO.., xiv,
    1, 9, 13, 16, 18, 19, 80, 82, 83, 85, 86, 95,
    99, 107, 122, 123, 125, 135, 137, 140,
    149, 161, 167, 169
Hill, Captain Peter, R.N., xiv, 26, 122
Hill, Miss Jean, 26
Hippo, xiv, xvii, 28, 29, 54
HMS *Alynbank*, 119, 120, 121
HMS *Aristocrat*, vii, 113, 114, 117, 118,
    119, 120, 121, 157, 158, 167, 169
HMS *Barham*, 34
HMS *Darthema*, 96, 99
HMS *Despatch*, 117, 118, 120
HMS *Dolphin*, 96, 99
HMS *Fury*, 158
HMS *Pelorus*, 111
HMS *Resolve*, 157
HMS *Rodney*, 153
HMS *Vivacious*, 128
Holloway Bros., 28
Hughes, Iorys, 28
Hughes-Hallett, Vice Admiral, xiv, 2, 22,
    79
Hunt, Major Edwin, vii, xiv, 92
Isle of Whithorn, 26
Jarman, Lt. W D, xiv, 129
Kerensky, O, 20, 21
King, Admiral Ernest, US Navy, vii, xiv, 8,
    15, 16, 19, 22, 55, 61, 101, 116, 130, 169
Kintyre, 96
Kite anchor, 35, 152
Largs Conference, 3, 4, 17
LCTs (Landing Craft Tanks), 129, 131, 132
Le Havre, 2, 89, 95, 148
Leathers, Lord Frederick Alan, xiv, 122
Leith, 38, 41, 42, 50, 51, 60, 107, 124, 169
Lochryan, 102, 103
LST (Landing Ship Tank), xviii, 32, 71, 89,
    141, 147, 149, 151, 153, 154
LSTs, xvii, 32, 71, 131, 148, 151
Lucayan, 29, 45
Luck, John, xiv, xv, 115, 116, 125, 128,
    136, 137, 138, 139, 153
Mais, Lt. Col. Raymond, xiii, xv, 40,
    113–117, 121, 136–142, 150, 153, 154
Marchwood, 83, 92, 105, 106, 124
Marshall, General, xiv–xvi, 7, 8, 110
McCallie, Archie, 29
Ministry of Supply, 13, 16, 20, 21, 38, 86,
    92, 105, 109
Ministry of Transport, 101

Monckton, Sir Walter, 163, 164, 167, 169
Montgomery, Gen. Sir B, 86, 88, 110, 160
Morgan,. Gen. Sir Frederick, xv, 1, 3, 4, 18,
    22
Motherwell, vii, xv, 30, 38, 169
Mulberry, i, iii, vii, ix, xi, xiii–xviii, 4,
    6–18, 20–23, 25, 26, 29, 31, 33, 35–40,
    70–74, 79–82, 84–88, 90, 91, 93, 95,
    101, 106–109, 111, 113–115, 117, 119,
    121–123, 125, 126, 128, 132, 135, 136,
    141–158, 160, 161, 163, 164, 167
Mulberry A, xviii, 8, 70–74, 106, 126, 135,
    136, 142, 144–148, 150–152, 154
Mulberry B, xv, xviii, 8, 74, 88, 106, 111,
    117, 121, 126, 135, 136, 144–154, 157,
    163
Newhaven (Fife), 103
Normandy beaches, 7, 123
Oban, xiv, 122
Omaha, 3, 70, 71, 96, 109, 116, 119, 126,
    127, 135, 147–151
Overlord, xviii, 1, 3, 8, 10, 38, 79, 109, 129,
    155
Paget, General, 4, 21
Penney, Prof. W G (Imperial College), 7
Petrie, Capt. C H, RN, xv, 90, 117, 118,
    119, 120, 150
Petrie, Capt. C H., R.N., xv, 90, 117, 118,
    119, 120, 150
Phoenix/es, x, xiii, xvii, xviii, 12–14, 16,
    18–21, 23, 79, 80, 81, 83–85, 87–93,
    101, 104, 107, 108, 121–126, 143–145,
    149–156, 163
Piers, floating bridge/roadway, ix, 25, 27,
    83, 126
Pintar, Robert, vii, 126, 128
Polglaze, Richard, vii, 117, 157, 167
Poole, 107, 123
Port-en-Bessin, 112, 116, 146
Portland, 123
Portsmouth, 20, 90, 99, 122, 124, 129, 131,
    156
Portyerrock Bay, 26, 27, 29
QAIMNS, Queen Alexandra's Imperial
    Military Service, xviii, 158, 161
Quebec, 4, 7–11, 13–17, 79
Queen Mary, 8, 79
R.N., 2, 13, 16, 82, 122–124, 126
Ramsay, Admiral Sir Bertram, vii, xv, 3,
    18, 20, 23, 81, 107, 111, 150, 154
Renfrew, xiv, xvi, 6, 29, 111
Richborough, 92, 105, 106, 124
Rigg Bay, 25, 26, 28, 29, 54